Experiments with Solar Energy

Other books by D. S. Halacy, Jr.

COMING AGE OF SOLAR ENERGY

COMPUTERS: THE MACHINES WE THINK WITH

COPTER COWBOY

DUSTER PILOT

FABULOUS FIREBALL

HIGH CHALLENGE

NINE ROADS TO TOMORROW

THE ROBOTS ARE HERE!

ROCKET RESCUE

WHALE SPOTTERS

STAR FOR A COMPASS

SURFER!

RIPCORD

CYBORG: EVOLUTION OF THE SUPERMAN

BIONICS: THE SCIENCE OF "LIVING" MACHINES

RETURN FROM LUNA

Experiments with Solar Energy

D. S. Halacy, Jr.

Illustrated with photographs and line drawings

W · W · NORTON & CO · INC · NEW YORK

Contents

LIST OF ILLUSTRATIONS

Experiments with Solar Energy

1

Meet the Sun

IT'S NO SECRET that the sun provides the energy that
keeps us alive. Solar heat keeps us warm, grows our
food, and makes our weather; without sunlight we
would be blind. But beyond these most important basic
purposes, solar energy has additional potential we will
one day harness. There are many simple applications
that demonstrate this potential, and this book is your
invitation to the fun of putting solar energy to work in a
variety of useful ways. In the chapters that follow there
are plans for solar cookers, a radio, a water heater, a
furnace, a model airplane that flies on sunshine, and
other projects that will give ample reward for the time
spent on them. Before we begin to assemble a solar oven
or a radio powered by a sun battery, let's take a brief
look at solar energy to see why it is so fascinating and
challenging.

The use of silicon cells, or some other type of "solar
battery" to convert sunshine into electricity, is an ex-

Solar batteries power satellites that detect nuclear blasts.
NASA

ample of the great strides being made in the solar-
energy field. Until a few years ago the sun battery
wasn't much more than a hopeful gleam in the eyes of
research scientists. Now the batteries exist. Today radio
receivers are picking up the steady signals generated
by silicon cells carried on spacecraft. Meanwhile, back
on earth, transistor radios powered by sunlight have
been introduced. Of course these radios will operate in

artificial light too, and some of them even store up sun energy during the day for evening use.

When we understand the amazing accomplishments of the sun battery in the few years it has been with us, it is easy to understand why it is the best-known use of solar energy. Able to tap directly the vast reservoir of "free" power the sun beams at us, the sun battery is assured of an important role in man's conquest of space.

Building and operating a solar radio will give you only a glimpse of the many and varied possibilities of the solar cell. For example, electricity is a convenient method not only of using solar power but of storing it too. Sun batteries thus offer a practical twenty-four-hour source of energy when coupled with proper storage batteries. The maximum efficiency of commercial solar cells now available and in use is about 12 percent. In other words the battery is able to convert 12 percent of the solar energy beamed upon it into electric energy. Laboratory results have run as high as 14 percent; radiation physics indicates a theoretical maximum of 22 percent. Even at the 12 percent figure, a roof of solar batteries could easily power the most "electrified" home with only a week of clear weather a month!

The drawback, of course, is the present price of solar cells. The rooftop installation we talked about for electrifying a home would involve an outlay of many thousands of dollars, prohibitive except for millionaire solar enthusiasts. However, since the silicon used in the cells is one of the most plentiful elements on earth, the price may be drastically reduced in the future. In the meantime, don't despair. The cells we'll need for our solar projects cost only a few dollars and will last for many years, with proper care.

Early techniques for using the sun to drive engines were crude by our standards, but pioneer solar engi-

Solar-powered hot-air engine built by John Ericsson a century ago.   SOLAR ENERGY SOCIETY

Solar exhibit at Casablanca. Shown are projects similar to those in this book.
SOLAR ENERGY SOCIETY

neers like John Ericsson built hot-air engines almost a hundred years ago. The output of these primitive machines was low, but the challenge of "free" energy was strong. Each square yard of the earth's surface receives about 1,000 watts of power during sunlight hours. Some simple reflectors convert about half of this to useful heat, and when we consider that one horsepower is roughly 700 watts, the possibilities are exciting.

Lake Mead, the giant reservoir behind Boulder Dam, receives more sun energy on its surface than its waters develop as they cascade down to the huge hydroelectric generators! At present this solar energy is wasted, but when we learn how to make use of such sun power we will not need to worry about running out of fuel.

Aside from laboratory test engines, working solar pumps are being produced. Huge sun-heated steam plants have been proposed. What will finally be the most economical solar-power plant may depend on the findings of a new generation of scientists. Whatever form the plant takes, it will use the same energy source as our simple solar-battery-operated electric motor. A motor that will fly a model airplane on sunbeams!

Although the solar battery and other sun-*power* devices are used most often presently, they represent only one of several methods by which we can convert sunlight into usable energy. High in the Pyrenees Mountains of southern France is the Mont Louis solar furnace. Constructed just after World War II, this huge installation is 35 feet in diameter and is used in high-temperature research. It develops temperatures of thousands of degrees and smelts metals and other materials for industry. An even larger solar furnace is being built in France. It is 100 feet high! At present the only American solar furnace the size of the Mont Louis mirror is one operated by the United States Army Quartermaster Corps at Natick, Massachusetts.

A fully equipped solar furnace 5 feet in diameter developing 6,000 degrees Fahrenheit, and suitable for research or industrial use costs thousands of dollars. Larger ones, like that of the Army, cost far more, of course. Few of us could afford even the "small" 5 foot model, but we can build a solar furnace with a lens 14 inches in diameter which is capable of producing a temperature of 2,000 degrees F. or more. That temperature will melt a number of metals and can be used for

Giant solar furnace nearing completion at Odeillo, France, will be world's largest. It is expected to develop about 2,000 thermal kilowatts. Huge parabolic reflector is actually a nine-story building.
DR. FELIX TROMBE

soldering, light brazing, tempering, and annealing. An excellent use for our furnace is the firing of enameled jewelry.

Not nearly so spectacular as solar furnaces, but perhaps of more importance in the long run, are solar homes and sun-heated buildings that are being developed. Heat is a logical thing to get from the sun, but engineers plan to produce the opposite as well; refrigeration systems powered by the sun have shown promise in tests, and solar plants have produced ice in sizable quantities!

The sun is also very effective in the distillation of

This 30,000 square foot solar still, built in the town square on the Greek Island of Symi, produces about 6,000 gallons of fresh water a day.
SOLAR ENERGY SOCIETY

water. Taking a tip from South Americans who operated a solar still long ago to produce thousands of gallons of drinkable water a day in a region having no fresh water, engineers are now desalinating sea water for domestic use in areas of water scarcity. There are a number of solar stills operating on arid Greek islands, for example. Places like Israel and our own southwestern deserts could profit by successful application of such stills.

Our do-it-yourself solar still has a collection area of about 4 square feet. Distillation of sea water—to alleviate shortages caused by the dwindling usable supply and increasing population—will require *acres* of surface, together with special plastic materials with an efficiency of light transmission higher than that of materials now available. In principle, however, the small model we will build is much the same as the pilot plants already built and the full-scale installations to come. It will distill salty or otherwise unfit water, making it suitable for drinking or for use in batteries, steam irons, and so forth, or for experimental purposes.

One commercially available solar-reflector cooker costs about 30 dollars. It is well worth the money and, since it folds compactly, is fine for taking along on picnics and camping trips. Our simpler cardboard cooker is much homelier and doesn't have the advantage of portability. To offset these disadvantages, however, it is much less expensive and quite easy to build. Costing about five dollars, it is made from cardboard and aluminum foil. Yet it will cook hot dogs in ten minutes or boil a quart of water in a little over half an hour, with no time lost to get the fire going!

When you tire of steak, hotcakes, and so forth, there is a solar oven to take care of another kind of cookery. This project is a real oven and uses the "greenhouse" principle to trap the sun's heat. Our oven reaches 400 degrees F. and will bake bread, casseroles, meat dishes, and even pies. It, too, costs only a few dollars.

Solar hot-water heaters have been with us for some time, but today they are better designed. Some swimming-pool owners heat their pools this way for winter swimming. The water heater we will build provides a

Solar water heater mounted on rooftop in Israel.
SOLAR ENERGY SOCIETY

modest supply of hot water for camp or cabin. It uses principles familiar to engineers and architects—those of conduction and convection, and a handy phenomenon called *thermosyphoning.*

So great are the long-range possibilities of solar energy that scientists have called the sun our "peaceful H-bomb." Fortunately, to build solar devices we don't have to be skilled engineers and millionaires as well, as we would have to be to construct a nuclear machine. As a matter of fact, each of the projects presented here is within the mechanical ability of nearly anyone and won't strain even the most modest pocketbook.

The so-called "solar belt" extends from the equator to the fortieth parallels of latitude, and solar devices will work in most of the populated areas of the world. Of course, the more sunshine, the more efficient the device; and the sun high overhead is stronger than when it is low on the horizon. But even as far north as Montreal a solar home has proved its worth. Chances are that unless you are a resident of the polar regions, there will be enough sunlight available to operate the project of your choice.

In addition to the sun projects presented here, there are others that are interesting and thought-provoking. The sundial, for instance, is the earliest form of solar clock. The radiometer, is a sun motor in its simplest form and yet suggests one of the most fantastic space-travel concepts that has yet been considered. There are also electric clocks, cigarette lighters, and hearing aids using solar fuel. All these things, and more, are no longer dreams of science-fiction writers but a reality. In a few days you can have the sun working for *you*, with one or more of the projects in this book.

You will find all of our projects easy. They require no special skills or expensive tools, and their cost is small. Yet, though they are simple, they demonstrate the theories of solar science. In building those of your choice you may well acquire the curiosity to delve deeper into

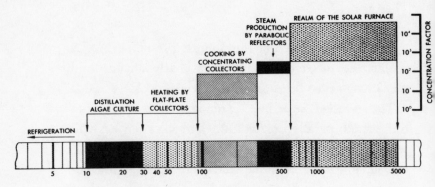

Thermal applications of solar energy.
SOLAR ENERGY SOCIETY

the fields of thermodynamics, optics, electronics, and mechanics. This is the way it should be. Good luck, and have fun with the sun!

2

Solar Furnace

THE IMPORTANCE of solar heat is obvious and the expression "a place in the sun" has roots in our vital need for warmth. At times the sun seems to produce too much heat and we swelter and turn brown in its rays. But heat is useful to man in many ways. Since it is the easiest of all the kinds of radiation from the sun to harness we shall begin our projects with a solar furnace: an optical device that increases temperature as lenses enlarge images.

Most of us learned at an early age that a magnifying glass would do more than simply enlarge the image of type in a book. A lens can magnify heat as well; that is, it concentrates the sun's rays into a small space. By merging a relatively large amount of warm rays into a small hot point, we can use the hot point to burn our initials in wood, start a campfire, or, as with our reflector stove, cook a meal. It is this same principle of concentration that makes possible the huge solar furnaces in operation today. A lens or mirror, whichever the case may be, intercepts a certain amount of sunlight and focuses all of its energy onto a tiny spot. This can produce temperatures of several thousand degrees Fahrenheit.

Centuries ago, scientists melted metals at temperatures in the neighborhood of 2,000 degrees F., even with the comparatively crude furnaces they were able to construct. Modern technology has made it possible for the solar furnace to create the hottest temperatures available to man for any appreciable length of time. Other methods such as the "shock tube" and plasma-jet techniques, too complex to discuss here, do produce higher temperatures, but only at great cost and for limited periods of time.

Lavoisier's solar furnace used two lenses instead of mirrors, and reached temperatures approaching 2,000 degrees F.
SOLAR ENERGY SOCIETY

Large solar furnace built by U. S. Army. Used for materials re-
search, it is capable of 5,000 degree F. temperatures and can
burn a 4 inch hole in an iron I-beam.
U. S. ARMY PHOTOGRAPH

France's 35-foot solar furnace has operated for many years and has satisfactorily melted metals experimentally and for industrial use. The furnace of the U.S. Army Quartermaster Corps is about the same size and is used for testing materials.

Obviously these furnaces cost fortunes to erect, but anyone can build a workable solar furnace for a few dollars and in a few hours. Far from being a toy, this furnace will melt metals with fairly low melting points, do soldering jobs, and even heat a kiln for firing ceramic jewelry.

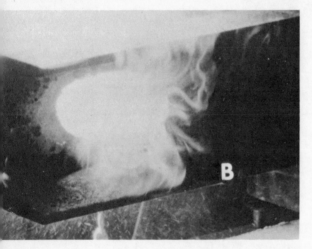

Graphic presentation of the intense heat the Army Quartermaster Research & Engineering Command's new solar furnace can generate is made by these sequence photos taken during an operational test at the Natick (Mass.) site. Sunshine can be concentrated to reach sustained temperatures of nearly 5,000 degrees Fahrenheit.

In 1770, the French scientist A. L. Lavoisier had convex lenses made especially for him by the great St. Gobain glass works. These curved pieces of glass were joined together at their rims and filled with wine to make them equivalent to solid lenses. Light passing through them was refracted or bent toward a common focal point to heat whatever samples the scientist placed there.

A convex glass lens of the size needed for our furnace would far exceed the average budget but fortunately there is a substitute, a thin, grooved piece of plastic which takes the place of the thick lens. Called a Fresnel lens, this will serve our purpose well.

As the sketch on this page shows, the curved surface of the lens is, in effect, cut into small segments of equal

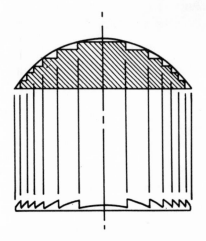

CURVED SURFACE
DIVIDED INTO STEPS

FRESNEL LENS

height and flattened out into the thin form shown. Plastic Fresnel lenses are made for a reasonable price from a master form. The one used in our project costs six or seven dollars. It produces about 300 degrees of temperature for each dollar spent!

We could immediately use our lens for melting, soldering, and so forth, much as we would use a smaller burning lens. But holding the lens in one's hands and trying to keep it accurately focused on the work would soon tire the most ardent experimenter. A necessary part of our furnace, then, is the lens mount.

To understand the use of the equatorial mount, consider how the sun moves across the sky during the day. The earth rotates on its north–south axis, and the apparent movement of the sun is at right angles to this axis, that is, it rises in the east and sets in the west. (This is a simplification, and readers familiar with astronomy know the actual movements are somewhat more complicated.) The sun moves along a "parallel of latitude" in its daily journey. We are acquainted with the gradual movement of the sun south in wintertime, but now we are considering just one day's solar motion.

For greatest usefulness our lens should "follow" the sun, and for this purpose the equatorial mount is ideally suited. Such mounts are used in telescopes, so designed that a motor turning at the right speed will keep a star or other body continuously in the field of vision. Large solar furnaces operate in this way or with a photoelectric device that keeps the sun's image properly positioned. Of course, in our simple solar furnace we will not include an automatic tracking system.

The equatorial mount has two axes. One of these is adjusted so that it is parallel with earth's north–south axis. When this is done, movement of the lens on the other axis (which is at right angles to the north–south axis) follows the sun.

Set up correctly, our furnace mount is so designed that we have only to tip the swinging part to follow the sun. In practice we will find that since the sun moves only about one degree in four minutes we can sometimes accomplish our soldering, melting, or other operation without moving the lens. Most often, however, the equatorial mount is more convenient.

Now that we have briefly discussed the theory of operation of our solar furnace let's get busy and build it. See that everything is on hand before you begin. The job will go faster and you will soon have your furnace in operation.

MATERIALS:

1 by 2 inch wood—approximately 20 feet
1 by 4 inch wood—approximately 9 feet
3/4 inch plywood—19 by 19 inches
1 inch wood screws—16
1/4 by 4 inch studs and wing nuts—six
1/4 by 2 inch bolts and wing nuts—four
14 inch (diameter) Fresnel lens—one

1/4 inch chuck—one
Firebrick—one
Window glass—1/8 inch thick; to fit lens (see text)

The furnaces shown in this chapter use a 14-inch diameter lens of about 1/16 inch thickness. Edmund Scientific Corporation of Barrington, New Jersey, sells a variety of sizes and thicknesses of Fresnel lenses in square and rectangular shapes. Select one at least 11 inches square and having a focal length of 16 inches or more. The thicker the plastic, the more rigid the lens. If the plastic is thick enough it may not be necessary to support it with glass as is done in the furnace we are describing. Prices for lenses suitable for our furnace will range from $6 for the 11 inch lenses to $7.50 for one about 12 by 16 inches. Naturally, the larger the lens, the more heat the furnace will develop.

The firebrick kiln may be of any type that will withstand the great heat developed at the focal point.

Use a good grade of wood for the various parts of the furnace. Cheap lumber is a poor economy, because warping will result in a second-rate finished product. In addition to the materials listed, we will need a drill, crosscut saw, keyhole saw, and screwdriver.

On the 19 inch square plywood lens-holder, mark the cutout for the lens. If you plan to use a rigid plastic lens, make this opening slightly smaller than the lens to allow for overlap. If you are using a thin lens sandwiched between glass panes, you can make the cutout

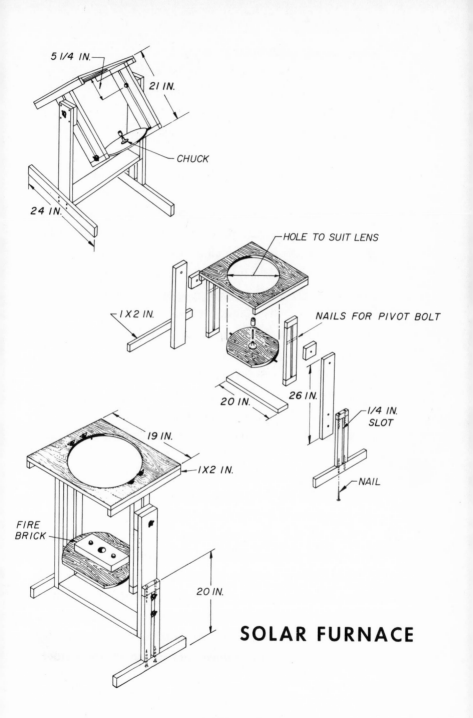

5 1/4 IN.

21 IN.

CHUCK

24 IN.

HOLE TO SUIT LENS

1 X 2 IN.

NAILS FOR PIVOT BOLT

20 IN.

26 IN.

1/4 IN. SLOT

NAIL

19 IN.

1 X 2 IN.

FIRE BRICK

20 IN.

SOLAR FURNACE

the exact size of the lens and let the glass overlap.

Drill a starting hole just inside the line, and use a keyhole saw to cut out the center. Save this piece of scrap for the worktable of the furnace on which we will later mount the kiln and adjustable chuck. Attach 1 by 2 strips to lens-holder, as shown on page 21.

Next cut the 1 by 2 strips that form the swinging frame, making sure all ends are square. Assemble with wood screws to form the slotted track that permits adjustment of the worktable. Drill holes in two places in each assembly for the finishing nails that form bearings for the pivot bolts. Double check to see that the slots are wide enough for the 1/4 inch studs to slide smoothly up and down, and set these parts aside.

Now drill four holes in the plywood lens-frame for the mounting studs as shown in the drawing. Carefully place the slotted parts in position and mark matching holes in their top ends. Drill for studs, and screw the studs in place. Leave enough threads protruding above the plywood for a washer and wing nut, plus several extra threads for mounting the lens in case you use the "glass sandwich" method to be described.

Next cut the three 1 by 4 pieces that form the yoke for holding the swing frame. Note that the dimension on the drawing for the base of the yoke is given as 20 inches. This is suitable for a 14-inch round Fresnel lens. If you use another size lens, adjust the length of the base piece accordingly. Assemble the yoke and nail the square spacer blocks in place on the top, inside surface

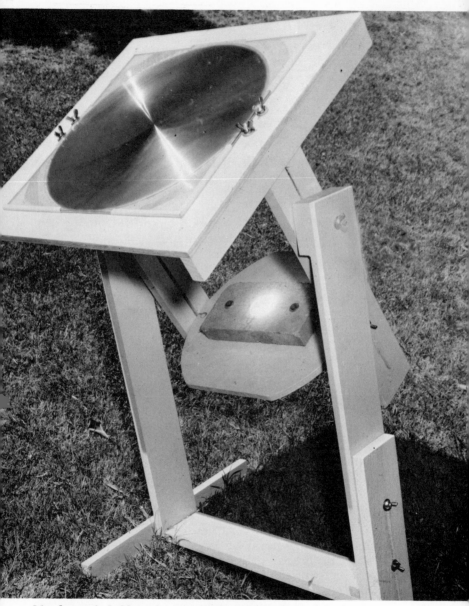

Metal sample held in chuck is oxidized by high temperature at focal point of furnace.

of the side pieces. Drill 1/4 inch holes for the pivot bolts through the sidepieces and spacer blocks. Attach the horizontal support with four wood screws so that the yoke will stand upright, and drill two 1/4 inch holes in the sidepiece opposite the horizontal support. These holes are for the bolts that hold the sliding adjustment leg, which is assembled of 1 by 2 strips in the same way as the swinging frame.

Now we can use the plywood piece left from the center of the lens holder. Trim the sides straight to eliminate the starting hole, and then drill two holes on opposite sides as shown in drawing to receive studs. Insert the studs. The worktable can now be attached to the side supports by means of washers and wing nuts.

Place the lens frame in position and slide the pivot bolts between the finishing nails to complete assembly of the mount. All that remains to be done is to install the lens. There are several ways of doing this. It is possible to glue a thin lens in place with Goodyear Plio-bond or a similar adhesive. An alternate method is to place the lens between two thicknesses of window glass and attach it to the lens frame by means of the washers and wing nuts.

If you want to use the gluing method, follow these instructions carefully: Remove the plywood frame from the mount and apply glue to the area to be covered by the lens. Several coats may be required to fill the pores of the wood. Add one more coat and let dry for a minute or so. This final coat should be brushed out

Solar furnace shows use of the firebrick

carefully so that it is uniform and not too thick; otherwise the plastic lens will not adhere properly and pull tight, as it should for best results.

Very gently place the lens in position on the frame, keeping it smooth, but without trying to stretch it. Be sure that the grooved side of the lens is up, or the furnace will not operate! With the lens in place, set it aside to dry for a day.

Because the Fresnel lens is plastic and can easily be damaged, a good way to add to its life is to sandwich it between two sheets of glass of the proper size. The photographs show this method. When not in use the lens can be removed and stored for safekeeping. Another advantage is that the lens is held more nearly in a plane than it is in the gluing method. The glass does cut down slightly the amount of heat transmitted through the lens, so the choice is between high temperature and durability.

Some of the Fresnel lenses available are thick enough (almost 1/8 inch) to be quite rigid. If you have this type you may mount it without glue or glass panes, simply attaching the lens with wing nuts as shown.

If you plan to use the furnace only for soldering, jewelry work, and so on, you may want just the firebrick kiln. With a masonry drill, drill two holes in the brick and matching holes in the worktable. If you don't have such a drill, the brick can be wired in place. For jewelry work it is handy to drill or chisel a shallow hole in the brick to hold small pieces.

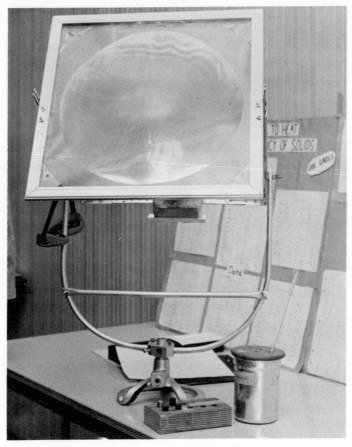

Fresnel lens mounted in simple U-frame. The unit can be used as a furnace.
SOLAR ENERGY SOCIETY

For experimental work it is also handy to have the adjustable chuck setup shown in the photograph. Metal samples are then easily placed at the focal point. A chuck from a discarded hand drill, along with a length of rod threaded to fit the chuck will serve the purpose. A mounting flange is screwed to the worktable to re-

Artist fires ceramic jewelry in solar furnace.
SOLAR ENERGY SOCIETY

ceive the rod, which may be adjusted to position the chuck as required. Both brick kiln and chuck may be left mounted on opposite sides of the worktable.

Using the furnace is simple. Place the mount with the adjustable leg toward the north (unless you live in the Southern Hemisphere), loosen the pivot wing nuts, and tip the lens frame toward the sun. *Wear dark glasses whenever you are using the furnace because the bright spot at the focal point can harm unprotected eyes.* Now move the adjustment leg until the image from the lens is centered on the worktable. It is a good idea to have the firebrick in place when setting up the first time, so that you won't burn holes in the worktable!

Tighten the wing nuts to hold the mount in place,

Samples of jewelry fired in solar furnace.
SOLAR ENERGY SOCIETY

and loosen those holding the worktable. Slide it back and forth until the bright spot in the firebrick kiln is at its smallest. The furnace is now focused, and the temperature should be close to 2,000 degrees F. with bright sun. You will understand now why we have made the table adjustable for purposely shifting focus for less heat. Experience will be the best teacher here. *Meantime, be careful of hands and eyes while you use the furnace.*

If you live in the north and use the furnace in winter, when the sun is low on the horizon, the equatorial mount must tilt considerably. It may be necessary to weight the base of the frame to prevent the furnace from tipping over. For short jobs, you may forget about orienting the base north and south and simply point the lens at the sun.

An alternate solar-furnace mounting makes use of this aiming system rather than the equatorial arrangement. For it we will need only a base plate and a pivoting U-frame. The lens holder is attached to the U-frame with studs and wing nuts. By properly tightening the fasteners, you can make the mount easy to position yet rigid enough to remain in place while you use the furnace. To keep the sun focused you will rotate the U-frame and tilt the lens-holder however much is required.

This simpler mounting will permit soldering, brazing, and similar operations but may require two sets of hands to hold everything in proper position!

3

Cardboard Cooker

OUR FIRST PROJECT was a furnace using a lens. Now we are going to build a stove. Instead of a lens, we use a reflecting mirror that also concentrates the sun's rays sufficiently to create cooking temperatures at its focus. A stove made of paper sounds about as practical as a pitcher carved from ice, but don't be fooled. Constructed almost entirely of cardboard, this reflector cooker will broil steaks, grill hot dogs, fry bacon and eggs, and make hotcakes and coffee. It will also heat water for doing the dishes. No fuel is necessary, because this stove cooks with sunshine!

Stop to think for a minute and you'll realize that every time we cook—be it with gas, electricity, or charcoal—we indirectly use the sun's energy, which has been stored up and reconverted to heat. Basically, then, our solar stove's fuel is nothing really new. Even the use of direct sun heat for cooking goes back many years. People have prepared sun-dried foods for hun-

A solar rice cooker produced by the Goto Company in Japan.
STANFORD RESEARCH INSTITUTE

dreds of years and crude solar stoves were built a century ago. Besides, who hasn't heard of cooking an egg on the sidewalk on a really hot day?

In recent years, however, many advances have been made in the design of solar cookers. Today there are commercial models that are fine for campers or for patio use. One umbrellalike design folds up for easy carrying and storage. Such a cooker is just the thing for trips. If you are dubious about how well the sun can cook a meal, or if you don't have the cash to buy a ready-made stove, get busy and build the one described on the following pages. At most, it will cost five dollars. If you use discarded cartons and other salvage material, the expense will be less.

MATERIALS:

Cardboard—as required
Poster board—two sheets
Aluminum foil—one roll
Plywood—one piece, 18 by 24 inches
1 inch aluminum tubing—approximately 64 inches
1 inch mounting flange—one
Grill—one
Curtain rod—one
1 x 2 wood—four feet
Clothesline—one foot
Glue—as required
Masking tape—as required
3/16 by 1 inch bolt with wing nut—one set

The reflector framework is cut from corrugated cardboard approximately 3/16 of an inch thick, the kind large cartons are made from. Some poster board and aluminum foil will complete the cooker itself. A grill stand (for hot dogs, hamburgers, or pans) is made from plywood, some tubing, and an inexpensive hand grill that costs about 50 cents.

Study page 37 first to get the over-all picture and to see how much new material will be needed. If you want to buy new cardboard, two 4 by 8 foot sheets will be plenty. These cost about 80 cents each at a box factory or supply house. The other items will be easy to find. Get all the materials ready and then begin construction. An eager beaver can do the job in a day or so and begin sampling outdoor cooking à la sun right away.

First, cut a base piece 3 feet square from the 3/16-inch cardboard. Mark the layout of the reflector ribs right on this base. This is the size our finished cooker will be. Next, draw two diagonal lines through the center of the base, perpendicular to each other, as shown on the plans. These mark the location of the main ribs, which we will make next.

A word about the principle of our reflector cooker will be helpful before we proceed. The sun stove focuses the sun's rays that strike its surface onto the bottom of the grill. Even on a clear winter day our cooker collects a lot of "warmth," which when shrunk into the 1 foot area at the grill, becomes concentrated "heat."

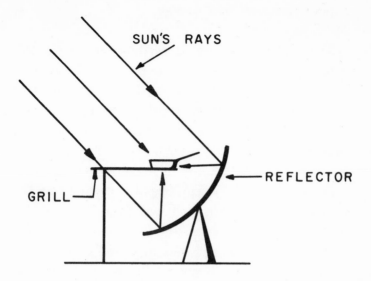

How solar-reflector cooker works.

The giant solar furnaces we talked of in the first chapter use curved reflectors too. They generate thousands of degrees at their focal points, using the same principle. To do this they must be of very accurate parabolic shape. This specially shaped curve reflects all the rays onto one tiny spot and gives the furnace a concentration ratio of many thousands to one. Obviously we don't want such high temperatures, for they would melt our pans!

Our reflector uses a radius of 36 inches instead of a true parabolic curve, resulting in a larger spot at the focal point. We will also use a number of wedge-shaped sections instead of one bowl-shaped reflector. Thus our focal spot will be roughly the size of the cooking pan, which is just what we want.

Now that we understand what we are doing, let's draw two main ribs as shown on the plans. To draw an accurate radius on the cardboard, drill two holes 36 inches apart in a strip of wood something over three feet long. Make one hole for a nail and another large enough to slip a pencil through. Drive the nail into a piece of wood that is firmly anchored and swing an arc with this king-size "pencil compass," making sure the plywood rib material is anchored down, too. Use this method on both full ribs instead of tracing one from the other, since the latter process may well result in discrepancies. Cut these ribs carefully, using a sharp linoleum knife, pocketknife, or model builder's razor knife. Be sure to plan ahead so as not to waste material as you lay out the ribs. Each of the main ribs has a notch at the center. Notice that one is on the top and one on the bottom so the ribs will interlock.

Using a full rib as a pattern, mark out twelve partial ribs, as shown on the plans. Before cutting these, cement the full ribs to the base plate on the lines previously drawn. Model airplane glue or a good household cement will work well. While the parts are drying, cut out the remaining ribs.

Notice that in addition to the full ribs which fit diagonally on the base plate, there are two other sizes. We will need four of the short, partial ribs and eight of the longer ones. These have the same 36 inch radius, but their inner and outer ends are trimmed to fit in the spaces allotted them on the base. Be very careful in

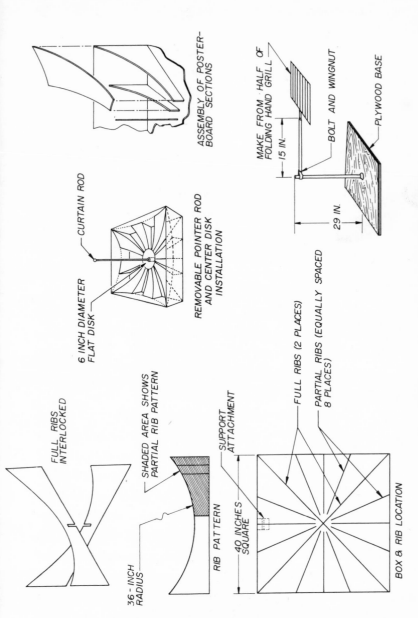

FULL RIBS
INTERLOCKED

36-INCH
RADIUS

SHADED AREA SHOWS
PARTIAL RIB PATTERN

RIB PATTERN

SUPPORT
ATTACHMENT

40 INCHES
SQUARE

FULL RIBS (2 PLACES)

PARTIAL RIBS (EQUALLY SPACED
8 PLACES)

BOX & RIB LOCATION

CURTAIN ROD

6 INCH DIAMETER
FLAT DISK

REMOVABLE POINTER ROD
AND CENTER DISK
INSTALLATION

ASSEMBLY OF POSTER-
BOARD SECTIONS

MAKE FROM HALF OF
FOLDING HAND GRILL

15 IN.

BOLT AND WINGNUT

PLYWOOD BASE

29 IN.

REFLECTOR SOLAR COOKER

cutting out the ribs. The effectiveness of the finished cooker will depend on your accuracy in cutting and installing the ribs, so take your time and do a good job.

When the framework is thoroughly dry, you are ready to put on the wedge-shaped pieces of poster board. Since these form the curve that will reflect the sun's rays, use poster board that is thin enough to bend easily, yet has sufficient body to hold the proper shape. Lighter cardboard would ripple and wave.

By means of cut-and-try methods, trim one piece of poster board so that it covers the space between two ribs, with about a 1/8 inch overlap all around. Do not cement this in place yet; it will be your pattern for more pieces. Cut them carefully, making sure they will cover any of the spaces between ribs. (In spite of care, there may be slight inaccuracies in the framework.) It is better to have the poster-board pieces a bit too large than too small.

There are two sizes of wedges to form the curve of the reflector. Make a pattern of each, and then cut out the others from these. Cut eight of each size. With all the pieces cut, now begin to cement them in place. Since butting the joints smoothly against each other would be difficult, glue eight pieces in alternate spaces first. Spread glue along the tops of two ribs, then lay the poster-board wedge in place and carefully press down so that it touches the ribs at all points. The glue will dry well enough in a minute or two so that you can go on to the next piece. Don't forget to leave every other section open.

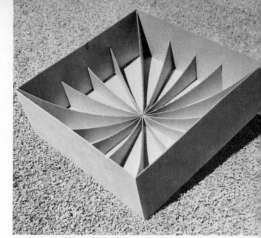

Ribs installed in box will support reflector.

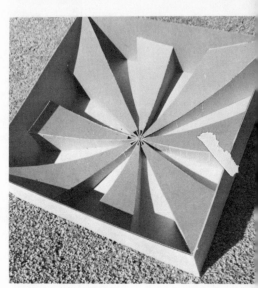

Half of the wedges are glued in place in the next stage of construction.

Completely covered reflector.

When these joints have dried, cover the open spaces with the remaining eight pieces of poster board. These will slightly lap over the edges of the pieces already glued in place, thus making a strong joint. At the center, where all the points come together, simply trim them off an inch or two. The hole left will later be covered with a separate piece of poster board.

It is possible to cover the reflector with aluminum foil from the handy kitchen roll of this material. But it is much easier to use foil already joined to a heavier paper backing. That used in the cooker described is aluminized Mylar plastic purchased from Edmund Scientific Corporation. Because of the strong paper backing it is easy to apply the foil smoothly. Use a cement of your choice: contact cement, household glue, rubber cement, or what have you. Again, the better the job you do the more efficient and durable your cooker will be.

Now install a marker for the focal point of the reflector so that you will know where to place the grill for the fastest cooking. This marker is simply a small, inexpensive curtain rod of the type used on kitchen doors. It consists of two tubes, one fitted inside the other. Cut a short length of the larger tube and insert it into a hole punched in the center of the reflector where the ribs come together. Better still, use a drill the same size as, or slightly smaller than, the tube to give a snug fit. Now cement the tube in place.

The smaller tube will fit into this "holder" and can be removed for easier handling when not needed. As men-

tioned before, the focal point of the reflector is the
proper place for mounting our grill. With a spherical
reflector the focal length is half the radius; in this case
18 inches. As a double check, aim the reflector at the
sun and adjust the tilt until there is no shadow visible
from the pointer rod. Then hold a piece of wrapping
paper with a small hole punched in it right at the tip of
the pointer. Move the paper toward the reflector and
then away from it until the smallest spot is observed on
the paper. This is the actual focal point, and the pointer
rod should be cut to this length.

Cut two small squares and one rectangle of cardboard, as shown by the dotted lines on the plans, and
cement them to the back of the cardboard base. The
squares go first, and then the rectangle. After these are

*Detail of the reflector support; nail in dowel engages loop
attached to cooker.*

well dried, run a short length of clothesline through the slot and tie the ends in a square knot. Drill holes through the 4-foot length of 1 by 2, spacing the holes about an inch apart halfway down the dowel. Insert a nail to engage the loop of clothesline. We can now set up our reflector so that it will stand alone.

To make the grill, first cut a plywood base 18 by 24 inches. Any thickness from 1/2 to 1 inch will do. Mark the center and install a mounting flange for the 1-inch

The reflector cooker in use. Rod indicates point at which heat is concentrated.

aluminum-tubing vertical support, which is 28 inches long. The adjustable arm is also aluminum tubing, 20 inches long. First, flatten one end and bend around a piece of pipe or a broomstick to make the collar, which fits over the vertical support. Drill a 3/16 inch hole in order to insert a bolt and a wing nut. The other end of the adjustable arm may now be flattened. Be careful to keep the flat area at right angles to the collar so that the grill will be horizontal when installed. Slide the grill in place and the solar cooker is complete.

Now that the work is done the fun starts. Positioning the reflector is simple if you follow these directions. Stand behind it and face it toward the sun. Now tilt it until the shadow of the pointer rod vanishes as it did when you checked for focal length. This means that the reflector is aimed properly and that the sun's rays will be bounced right where you want them.

Holding the reflector in this position, slip the 1 by 2 support through the rope loop and put the nail through the hole just below the loop. With the reflector on its own feet, you can now put the grill in place. Loosen the wing nut on the adjustable arm and move it up or down until the grill rests just above the tip of the pointer rod. As a double check, pass your hand quickly just above the grill. It should be hot, ready for you to start cooking.

The grill surface itself is fine for cooking hot dogs, burgers, or steak. Grease will drip on to the reflector but will not harm it. For bacon and eggs, hotcakes, and the like, place a skillet on the griddle. And if you like

Cooking hot dogs over larger solar device.

your steaks seared quickly to keep in the juice, use the
skillet for them, too. By putting it on the grill a few
minutes early you can store up extra heat that will cook
the steak more rapidly.

Water for coffee, tea, or for dishwashing can be
heated in a kettle or pot. To get the maximum efficiency
from your solar cooker, use blackened utensils; however, just about any kind will work satisfactorily. For
variety try a pressure cooker.

As the sun moves across the sky, the position of the
reflector must change. In early morning or late after-
noon it will be nearly vertical, while at noon in mid-
summer you may have to place it nearly flat on the
ground. That's why we drilled so many holes in the
support rod. If you plan to boil beans or make stew,
occasional adjustment of the reflector will be required
to keep the hot spot where it will do the most good. The
shadow from the pointer rod is the thing to watch. For
bacon and eggs, hot dogs, and even steak, one setting
will often do the trick.

After cooking your meal and washing the dishes, remove the grill from the aluminum tube and clean it,
too. Then wipe off the reflector surface with a paper
towel or damp cloth and that's all there is to the job of
solar cooking.

Solar stoves won't take the place of other kinds of
cooking all the time. When the sun goes down you had
better be through cooking, and on a rainy day the reflector is not much use except maybe to crawl under to

keep dry! But properly used in clear weather it will amaze the most skeptical observer. Here are a few of the advantages of solar cooking.

As you discovered when you held your hand close to the focal point, there is no warming-up period with a solar stove—it is hot right away. By the time the fellow with the charcoal brazier gets a good bed of coals, you will be doing the dishes. Besides, he paid for his fuel while yours was free for the taking. And solar energy is available any place the sun shines: mountains, desert, beach, or your own backyard.

At first, the reflection from your cooker might be bothersome, and a pair of sunglasses will be handy. After practicing a while you'll learn where to stand so there isn't any glare, and by then you will have noticed how nice it is not to have your eyes full of smoke. Solar cooking is cool cooking, too, because the heat goes into the food on the grill and doesn't roast the person doing the cooking as well.

You won't need matches to get your cooker going, and there's no danger of setting anything on fire either. Since the solar cooker produces no open flame it may be used safely even in areas where cooking fires are not permitted because of dry conditions or other hazards. Lastly, there are no ashes or soot to contend with.

You will have a lot of fun cooking with sunshine. It's safe, it's clean, and it's free. Chances are you'll find it portable enough for your next camping trip. That way you won't be tied down to a fireplace and the bother that goes with it. So save up for a commercial folding cooker, or you might even put your ingenuity to work and build a version of the cardboard stove that folds to make it more portable.

4

A Solar Oven

THE "GREENHOUSE" effect is well known to those who grow plants in such structures and also to those who have left the windows of a car rolled up on a warm, sunshiny day. The result is aptly described as resembling an oven. That is what we are going to build in this chapter—a solar oven that will do a real job of cooking on a clear day, even in winter.

Cooking with sunshine is an ancient idea. Man has dried fruits and meat in the sun for ages, a kind of leisurely cooking with solar energy. Direct use of sunshine for cooking dates back more than a century. When Napoleon was looking for a convenient way to cook for desert troops, a French scientist named Augustin Mouchot produced a solar cooker that did the trick nicely. In our own country, Dr. S. P. Langley experimented with solar cookers atop Mount Whitney many years ago. Both these men used the so-called "hothouse" principle. A glass cover on a box admits heat

Solar scientist Dr. Maria Telkes demonstrates use of an aluminum cooker of her design.
SOLAR ENERGY SOCIETY

readily, then doesn't let it get back out. This is because the incoming heat is "shortwave" radiation and passes easily through the "optical window" of the glass, while the "long wave" reflected heat waves are blocked by the glass. The cover on a solar oven is thus a kind of one-way valve for solar energy.

In recent years the solar oven idea has been revived and suggested as a means of cooking in undeveloped areas short of fuel as well as for campers and hobbyists. However, most solar ovens are of metal and quite heavy and expensive. The author's original oven was of

How solar oven traps heat.

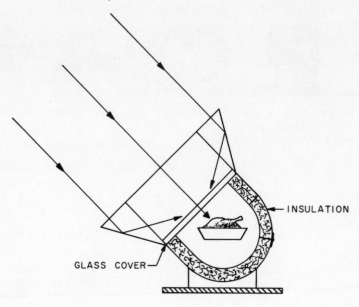

INSULATION

GLASS COVER

this type, built of galvanized iron insulated with fiber-glass. It cooked nicely, but was considerably more complicated to construct. The oven presented here takes care of such objections. It is light, compact, cheap, and very easy to build.

Our second project was a solar cooker made of cardboard. A solar oven is even more practical, particularly since it is more compact and not only cooks meat and vegetables, but bakes bread and cakes as well. We could make an oven from cardboard too, but for variety let's use another unlikely material. How about styrofoam plastic? Put a chunk of this stuff in the kitchen oven at the temperatures we hope to reach with our solar oven and in a few minutes all you'll have left is a little ball of melted plastic. So how can we bake at 400 degrees F. in a plastic oven? It's easy with some foil insulation inside and the cooling effect of the air outside the oven. The result is a cooker that is light and compact enough to take just about anywhere.

MATERIALS:

Styrofoam sheet—1-1/2 inches thick as needed
Glass—one piece, 1/8 inch thick, 13 inches square
Cardboard—as needed
Aluminum foil
Plastic cement
Cloth tape
Dowel—1/4 by 48 inches
Oven thermometer

The body of the oven will be made of foam plastic about 1-1/2 inches thick. Buy a sheet of this material from a local supplier and you'll have enough for a couple of stoves. With a wood saw cut out two identical side pieces, a top, bottom, and back. Cement the pieces together with an adhesive that won't dissolve the plastic. The plastics dealer can provide this, or you can use Wilhold or a similar product.

When the oven body is assembled, add four strips of 1/8 by 1 inch balsa wood, as shown on the plan. These strips form the seat for the glass cover which is also the oven door. This is ordinary 1/8 inch window glass, hinged with cloth tape to the oven, and fitted with a tape handle for opening. Have glass cut to size and the edges beveled for safety.

Now we have a primitive form of the solar oven. As mentioned earlier, the pioneer designs by Mouchot and Langley were just boxes fitted with glass lids. The heat of the oven depends on the amount of radiation that gets into it, of course. By increasing the size of the glass-covered box you can collect heat. But there is another, simpler, way of doing the same thing. With reflector panels, which double as protective covers for the glass, you can bounce more solar radiation into the oven.

If we mounted a reflector at a 90-degree angle to the glass it would not do any good, since solar rays would go right by it. Suppose we mount the reflector at a 45-degree angle? Now the rays bounce off all right, but

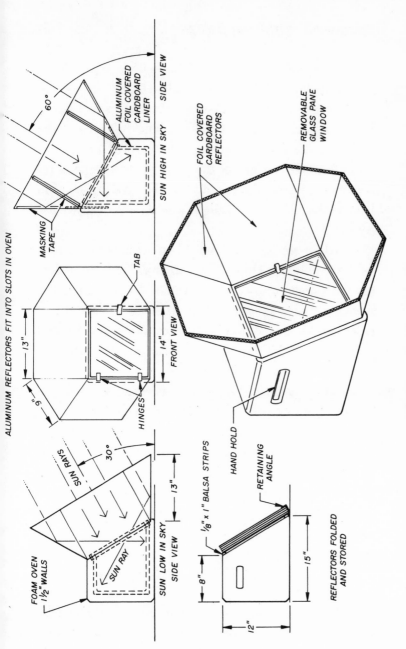

ALUMINUM REFLECTORS FIT INTO SLOTS IN OVEN

60°

ALUMINUM FOIL COVERED CARDBOARD LINER

SUN HIGH IN SKY   SIDE VIEW

MASKING TAPE

TAB

13"

14"

9"

FRONT VIEW

HINGES

FOIL COVERED CARDBOARD REFLECTORS

REMOVABLE GLASS PANE WINDOW

SUN RAYS

30°

13"

FOAM OVEN 1½" WALLS

SUN RAY

SUN LOW IN SKY   SIDE VIEW

⅛" x 1" BALSA STRIPS

HAND HOLD

RETAINING ANGLE

8"

15"

12"

REFLECTORS FOLDED AND STORED

SOLAR OVEN

they don't enter the oven. Instead they move parallel to the glass cover. This doesn't help either, but we are closer to a solution and all we need is the correct angle. If you're good at geometry you'll quickly arrive at the correct angle, 30 degrees from the vertical, or 120 degrees from the surface of the glass. At this angle, a reflector the same dimensions as the oven glass will bounce the radiation hitting it into the oven—just what we want.

A little more geometry will show us how much heat we have added with our one reflector. With the reflector at an angle of 30 degrees we add 50 percent to the amount of heat the oven alone gathers. If we add two reflectors, we double the heat. With four reflectors, and sections to fill the corners too, we can add two and one-half times the original heat of the oven.

Cut from cardboard four main reflectors and four triangular pieces to the dimensions on page 53. Cement on aluminum foil. Cloth tape serves as hinges for the triangular pieces and the main reflectors are mounted to the oven with dowels cemented to the reflectors, as shown. Simply push the dowels into the cardboard corrugations, liberally coated with glue, and let dry. Next drill or press holes into the oven itself at the proper angles to receive the dowels.

Line the inside of the oven with cardboard coated with "rippled" aluminum foil. This foil serves as insulation, while the wavy design cuts glare. Don't be tempted to use the "ripple" foil on the reflectors, however.

Compared with a conventional solar oven made of metal, this foam model is very easy to build and actually does as good a job or better. To use it, all you need do is set it on the ground in the sun and load it with food in the proper baking dishes or pans. Note that the shape of the oven is such that you have two choices of reflector angle. When the sun is low in the sky place the oven so that its glass cover is close to a right angle to the sun. When the sun is higher, set the oven on its "back" to catch more sun and heat. The glass door works easily in either position. When not in use, the cooker should be dismantled and the reflectors stored in the rack. This also protects the glass cover.

Left: The finished cooker is compact and light enough to be easily carried. Right: The glass cover of the oven opens easily to permit loading of food.

In case you can't find foam in bulk, you might try using a foam icebox, cut off at the proper angle and with a glass cover added. There are also other ways of making the reflectors. One of these is to use polished aluminum instead of cardboard covered with foil. Hinge the triangular corner pieces to the main reflectors as we did earlier. Then hinge the main reflectors to the body of the oven. Use cloth tape. Now the reflectors can be folded flat against the glass cover, protecting it and making the oven very compact. Fold bottom reflector first, then sides, and finally lower the top reflector.

To guard against the cooker being tipped over on a very windy day, add some wire U-shapes (like croquet wickets) that slide out from the bottom of the oven and can be weighted to anchor the oven.

The ovens described reach 350 degrees F. on a clear winter day and over 400 degrees F. in summer. To cook more food you can scale up the box and reflectors to half again the size shown. With a little effort and ingenuity a rack may be added to make more cooking space. The solar oven will bake bread, cook meat and vegetables, casseroles, and desserts. In a pinch you can use it to heat water too. It is even safer than the cardboard cooker; just don't burn your fingers on the glass door!

5

Water Heater

So FAR we have used solar heat to melt metals and to cook food. We can also heat water with solar energy. Such heaters have long been used, and as early as the 1930's southern California and Florida abounded in glass-covered heat collectors containing heating coils and a storage tank for hot water. Perhaps you have seen a solar water heater mounted atop a home.

The crude, makeshift designs of earlier days did a fair job of providing free hot water for domestic use, although standby heat sources were necessary for cloudy days or nighttime use. Today there are thousands of scientifically designed and highly efficient solar water heaters—particularly in Japan and Israel, where they compete successfully with gas and electric heaters.

In our solar oven we trapped heat inside the glass-covered box and then transferred that heat to the food we wanted to cook. In a water heater the heat transfer

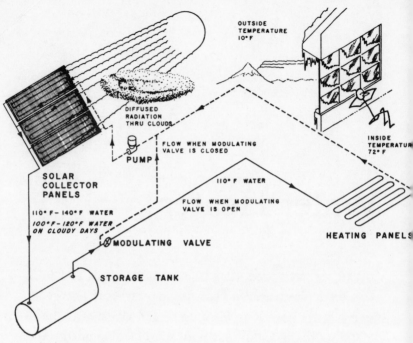

OUTSIDE
TEMPERATURE
10° F

DIFFUSED
RADIATION
THRU CLOUDS

FLOW WHEN MODULATING
VALVE IS CLOSED

PUMP

INSIDE
TEMPERATURE
72° F

SOLAR
COLLECTOR
PANELS

110° F WATER

FLOW WHEN MODULATING
VALVE IS OPEN

110° F - 140° F WATER
100° F - 120° F WATER
ON CLOUDY DAYS

MODULATING VALVE

HEATING PANELS

STORAGE TANK

Large solar water heater can create enough heat to keep a building warm.
BRIDGERS & PAXTON

is to water. The sun's rays warm water even without a special heating device. By adding a coil inside our hot box and circulating the water as it is warmed, we can make a more efficient water heater.

The heater described in this chapter is not intended for domestic use, but the 5 gallon tank would make a good supply for camping trips or for a cabin that has no provision for hot water. If desired, an enlarged version of the heater could be installed on a roof, connected to a water supply, and used as a permanent hot-water source.

MATERIALS:

1 by 4 inch wood—8 linear feet
1/2 inch plywood—two pieces 24 by 24 inches
Single-weight window glass—one piece, cut to measure
3/8 inch O. D. copper tubing—approximately 16 feet
Sheet metal—22 by 22 inches (copper or galvanized
    iron)
1/2 inch copper tubing—3 inches
1/2 inch valve—one
3/4 inch hose fitting—one
5 gallon can—one
3/8 inch I. D. plastic tubing—10 feet
1/4 by 1-1/2 inch wood screws—approximately thirty
Flat black paint—one pint
1/4 inch stud and nut—one each
Carrying handle—one

Begin the heater with the collector box itself. Make
the sides of the box from 1 by 4 material. At the lumberyard have a groove cut 1/8 inch wide to a depth of
3/8 of an inch in the 1 x 4 board. Locate the cut 1/2
inch from one edge. This is the slot for the glass window. The next step is to cut the pieces to the proper
length, being sure to keep the ends square both ways.
The glass should fit snugly. Cut out a square of plywood
24 inches on a side and place the 1 by 4 pieces on it to
make sure they fit. Assemble the sidepieces to the back
with wood screws.

SOLAR WATER HEATER

HOT WATER OUTLET

½ IN. TUBING

COLD WATER INLET

HOSE FITTING

3/8 IN. TUBING

VALVE

CONNECT A' TO A AND B' TO B WITH PLASTIC TUBING

A

B

C

PLYWOOD BACK

24 IN.

½ IN. HOLES

LEFT SIDE

WOOD PART PATTERNS

GROOVE TO RETAIN GLASS

4 IN. (TYPICAL)

30°

1 IN. SPACERS AT CENTER & CORNERS OF SHEET METAL

SHEET METAL

GLASS COVER

STAND

NOTE:
PAINT TUBING, SHEET METAL, & CAN FLAT BLACK.

TUBING SOLDERED TO SHEET METAL

REFLECTOR ALUMINUM FOIL COVERED

A'

B'

Take the box apart at this point and clean chips and shavings from the holes. Drill two 1/2 inch holes in one of the sidepieces, as shown on the drawing. These holes accommodate the copper tube coil which will carry water from the tank to the collector and back again. Now cement aluminum foil to the inside surface of the plywood base. This reflective material serves to bounce back radiated heat so that it will not be wasted.

Next, five small spacer blocks (1 inch cubes) are nailed into place, as shown on the drawing. Make these blocks the same thickness as the distance from the edge of the 1 by 4 piece to the 1/2 inch holes so that they hold the coil the proper distance from the plywood base. Small nails will be fine for attaching the spacers, but drill a hole through each block first to prevent splitting of the wood.

With the box itself completed, you can begin work on the copper coil and the collector plate. These are important parts of the heater, since they transfer heat from the sun to the water inside the coil. Copper is a very good conductor and will quickly carry heat to the water. It is quite expensive, however, and you may want to substitute galvanized iron to cut the cost.

If you use a copper sheet, have it cut to the exact size. It is sold by weight, and there is no need to pay for scrap. Notice that the size specified allows 1/4 inch clearance all around the inside of the box. Before working with the copper sheet, trim a small piece from each corner at a 45 degree angle to prevent being cut by the sharp edges.

Bend the heating coil from 3/8 inch copper tube, the flexible kind that comes in a roll. The length called for in the list of materials allows for trimming. First straighten out the tubing, making it as flat and true as you can. It is quite soft, and a little time spent should result in a smooth job. Now lay the tube across the flat sheet of copper, with the proper length extending beyond the edge. Mark the start of the first bend in the tubing with a pencil and then carefully form it with your fingers into a U-shape. Work slowly and evenly so that you will not flatten the tube excessively.

After the first bend is made, replace the tubing on the sheet and make sure the bend is in the proper position and that sufficient tubing extends past the edge of the sheet. Mark the second bend and proceed as before.

Assembly of heat-collector tubing into foil-lined box.

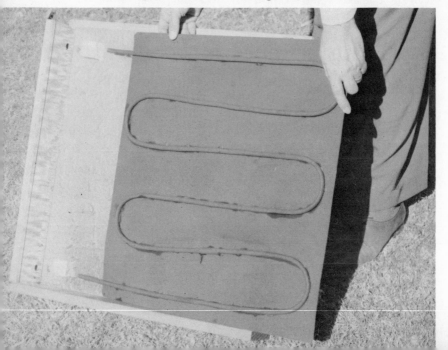

Continue to form the coil in this manner until the sheet is covered in a series of S-turns, as shown.

Trim the long end of the tubing; check the shape of the coil once more; and then lay it on a flat surface to see that it is level. Spend as much time as required to make the tubing lie perfectly flat, using your fingers and tapping lightly with a rubber or wooden mallet for the finishing touches. The tubing should touch the sheet along its full length for good heat transfer.

When you are completely satisfied with the job, solder the copper coil to the sheet. Clean the tube and the sheet with emery cloth so that the solder will stick properly. Lay the sheet on a wooden surface (the inverted collector box itself will do nicely), and place the coil in position. Remember that the ends of the tubing must fit through the holes drilled in the 1 by 4. Now lay a board over the coil, and weight it to keep the tubing in place. You are ready for the soldering operation. If you have built the solar furnace this would be a good time to try it out!

A small torch is handy for this purpose, and a soldering iron will do the job too. If you aren't equipped for such work, have it done at a sheet-metal shop. Solder as shown on the drawing, about 6 inches apart. Be sure to hold the tubing flat to the sheet. Heat may cause the copper to warp slightly, but it will return to its flat position upon cooling.

With the job completed, clean any excess soldering paste from the copper and paint the entire assembly flat black. Apply a second coat of paint for good measure and set it aside until it is completely dry. The coil assembly may then be slipped into the box, with the ends of tubing carefully inserted into the 1/2 inch holes. Tack the copper sheet to the spacer blocks when you are sure it fits properly and will not have to be removed.

Unscrew the top 1 by 4 piece. Slide a piece of cardboard into the grooves. Trim to fit and have your glass supplier cut to this measure. Fit the glass into the slots, and replace the top piece. When you install the carrying handle, the collector is complete and you can begin work on the water tank.

A round, 5 gallon can with narrow, screw-top spout is used for the storage of heated water. The one in the photograph was a discarded oil can obtained from a local distributor. Other types of containers are suitable and may be substituted if the round type shown is not available. For example, a square, lightweight can will fill the bill. This type is usually on sale at hardware and surplus stores.

Clean the can of any residue of oil or other liquid. This is done for two reasons. First, we don't want the water contaminated and, second, heat from soldering operations might set fire to the liquid. So do the cleaning carefully and flush with water several times.

Two short lengths of 3/8 inch copper tubing are soldered to the can. The location and dimensions are shown in the drawing on page 60. First drill a 1/4 inch hole in each place a tube is to be installed. Next drive a center punch or other tapered piece of metal into the hole. This enlarges the hole and also forces the metal inward. Check frequently during this flaring process to insure a snug fit of tubing. The depression formed in this way will hold more solder and make a stronger joint.

If a painted can is used, it will be necessary to scrape the areas where soldering is to be done. When the metal is clean and bright, insert the tubing (which has been cleaned too). Using a solar furnace, torch, or soldering iron, let solder flow into the depression and around the tube. This operation is easier if the can is positioned with the tube pointing straight up.

The hot-water outlet is also a length of 3/8 inch tubing soldered to the screwed-on cap of the can. Use the "flaring" method again so that a strong joint will result. Notice that the tube is bent into a U-shape.

You are now ready to do the plumbing for the cold-water supply line. Instead of 3/8 inch tubing, use 1/2 inch tubing for this connection. Attach a simple shutoff valve to the tube, using compression-type fittings that come with the valve. Your dealer will explain how these fittings are installed. Another short length of 1/2 inch tubing extends from the valve. The free end of this tubing is soldered inside a brass garden-hose fitting of the type used with a plastic hose.

With the soldered joint made and the compression fittings tightened securely, you can connect the tank to the end of the garden hose and check for leaks. Turn on the water at the faucet; open the valve at the tank; and cork the tubes that will lead to the collector. When the tank is full, water will overflow from the hot-water supply outlet. Mark any leaks, drain the tank, and repair as necessary. The tank is now ready to be attached to the collector coil.

Your heater would be of little use if only the water in the coil itself became hot; this would barely be enough to wash one's hands. If you made a very large collector, the coils would hold ample hot water. Another method would be to install a pump to circulate water between coils and tank. This would cost more money and also make the heater more complicated. Fortunately, there is a phenomenon called thermosyphoning, which will heat the whole tank of water. Thermosyphoning is the ability of water to circulate of its own accord when heated—given certain conditions. The most important of these conditions is that the supply tank be located *above* the coil.

The photograph shows the tank mounted on a stand, with the bottom of the tank about on a level with the top of the collector. As the coil heats water inside it, this water rises and is replaced by cooler water drawn from the bottom of the tank.

Using the hinged prop, set up the collector facing the sun. Then place the tank on its stand to one side. Install the plastic hose between the two bottom tubes, using hose clamps for a watertight connection if necessary. Attach one end of the second plastic hose to the upper

Drawing hot water from the solar water heater.

tube of the collector, but leave the other end free.

Fill the tank. When water flows from the open plastic hose, block the hose with your finger until water also flows from the top circulation tube of the tank. Then quickly slide the hose onto the tube and clamp it. This prevents air bubbles from being trapped in the lines. When the hot-water outlet overflows, close the tank valve.

Operation of the heater is simple. You will notice that the upper hose quickly gets hot, while the lower one stays relatively cool. Water is circulating now, and eventually all of it will be warmed by the coils. To draw hot water, open the valve at the bottom of the tank. Cold water comes in and forces hot water out of the top.

Water heater with reflector panel added.

To increase the heating capacity of your water
heater, add a reflector panel that will also serve as a protective cover for the glass when you store the heater.
One reflector, set at 30 degrees, will add 50 percent
more heat. You can add four, if desired, and greatly
increase the heating capacity. The water heater in the
photograph uses one reflector, hinged at the bottom
and secured at the top. A hole in the reflector fits over
the 1/4 inch stud and is held in place with a nut when

the heater is stored or being carried about.

Make the reflector(s) of 1/2 inch plywood, faced with aluminized Mylar, aluminum foil, or similar reflecting material. Attach to the heater with hinges, allowing one reflector to fold down on top of the other as shown on the drawing. Lengths of cord hold the reflector panels at the proper angle. As with the oven, when the reflector is closed it protects the glass cover of the heater.

You can use the heater in a more portable version, on a camping trip, for instance, where there is no water-pressure supply available. Simply close the inlet valve, fill the tank through the top, and let the water heat. To draw hot water, tip the tank and pour out water through the spout. Replace as needed.

You can very easily "scale up" the small heater presented here for use in a mountain cabin or a similar place that is not equipped with hot water. For example, a 50 gallon oil drum and a heat collector, 2 feet by 10 or 12 feet, mounted on the roof serves as a practical hot-water heater. Some swimming-pool owners have built their own solar pool heaters and saved the high monthly costs of gas-fired installations. A word of advice here: such an installation will require a very large area of heat collector (one-third or one-half that of the pool), properly oriented, and also a plumbing system, including a pump to circulate the water. A more challenging use of solar water heating is to heat a home or building instead of just its water supply!

Solar heater shown in drawing warms entire office building.
BRIDGERS & PAXTON

6

A Solar Still

NINETY YEARS AGO, mine owners in the high country of
Chile were faced with the problem of providing water
for their workers. The only available supply was unfit
to drink, and so a means of purifying it had to be found.
The solution was a sun-operated distilling plant in
which a large area of glass-covered wooden frames

*Solar still, located in the Andes Mountains in Chile in the
1870's, operated on the same principle we use in our project.*
SOLAR ENERGY SOCIETY

evaporated the contaminated water, recondensed it, and thus produced 6,000 gallons of fresh water a day!

This Chilean solar still used no fuel or power except that from the sun's rays and provided pure water at a cost far lower than other means of distillation. But the method was forgotten for many years and fuel-operated stills were used whenever it was necessary to convert salty or otherwise undrinkable water.

Not until World War II were solar stills used again, except by experimenters. Fliers forced down at sea needed a source of drinking water until they could be rescued. Dr. Maria Telkes developed an inexpensive, lightweight plastic still that could be included even in one-man life rafts to provide a quart of fresh water a day.

Since that time, Dr. Telkes and other scientists have worked with solar stills of various sizes. The United States Department of the Interior is interested in the method, and suggestions have been made for large sea-coast installations to purify salt water for drinking and irrigation. In some designs no pumps would be needed because the sea itself would fill the distillation tanks at high tide.

At present the cost of such a system is high, even considering that its operation would be cheaper than a fuel-run still. Engineers are hopeful, however, that improved methods and materials will make solar distillation economically competitive. Meanwhile, there are large experimental installations in Florida, Mexico,

Plastic inflatable solar stills were developed for use in World War II by Dr. Maria Telkes.
SOLAR ENERGY SOCIETY

This solar still at Puerto Penasco, Mexico, was constructed by the University of Arizona and the University of Sonora. Its 12,000 square foot solar-heat collectors produce about 6,000 gallons of fresh water a day.
UNIVERSITY OF ARIZONA

Australia. On a number of Greek islands they are an important source of fresh water for the inhabitants.

The principle of the solar still is simple, and is observed on a grand scale in nature. Clouds are composed of water vapor evaporated from the surface of the sea or from damp ground and then condensed by cool temperatures high in the air until it becomes visible. In the process of evaporation, salt and other solids are left behind. Many readers will be familiar with the commercial harvesting of salt in shallow ponds, for this is one of the oldest of man's uses of solar energy. In solar stills the salt is a waste product, and we recover fresh water that is allowed to escape in the salt-pond operation. In the water heater, solar heat warmed the water in the coils. Since the water was enclosed in the coils and tank, little of it evaporated. However, in the still, the water is allowed to evaporate. Water vapor rises and contacts the underside of the glass cover. Here it condenses because the glass is cooler than the vapor. Gravity causes the droplets to run down the glass, along the bottom of the box, and out through the drain tube. Salt —or other pollutants—remain in the wick of the still or drain out in brine that is not evaporated.

The design has been proved by careful testing over a long period of time. Researchers have shown that it is possible to produce almost a quart and a half of water a day for each square foot of the collector's surface. Thus the still should have a maximum output of more than one gallon a day. Of course, this figure represents ideal conditions, but it will be interesting to compare your

This solar still produces fresh water from salty or otherwise contaminated water.

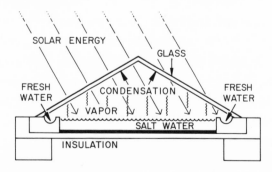

results with it. The still described here was tested in midwinter, and produced more than one quart of fresh water in six hours.

MATERIALS:

1 by 4 inch redwood board—8 linear feet
1/2 inch plywood—two pieces, 24 by 24 inches
Single-weight window glass—one piece, cut to measure
1/2 inch O. D. copper tubing—4-1/2 feet
1/2 inch, 90 degree copper elbow—one
1/2 inch copper pipe cap—one
Galvanized iron—one piece, 3 by 24 inches
1/4 inch I. D. copper tube—6 inches
Large tin can—one
1/4 by 1-1/2 inch wood screws—approximately thirty
Black terry cloth—approximately two yards (one large bath towel)
Carrying handle—one

To begin construction, first assemble all the needed materials (except the glass). Redwood is preferred where possible because it resists rotting, while other woods will deteriorate with constant exposure to water.

At the lumberyard where you buy the 8 foot board (1 by 4 inches) have a groove cut 1/8 inch wide to a depth of 3/8 inch. Locate the cut 1/2 inch from one edge. This is the slot for the glass window. Next cut the

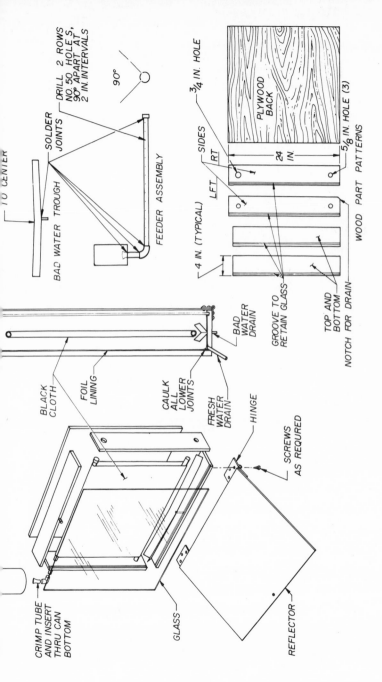

DRILL 2 ROWS
NO. 50 HOLES,
90° APART AT
2 IN. INTERVALS

90°

SOLDER
JOINTS

BAD WATER TROUGH

TO CENTER

FEEDER ASSEMBLY

PLYWOOD BACK

3/4 IN. HOLE

SIDES

RT

LFT

24 IN.

5/8 IN. HOLE (3)

WOOD PART PATTERNS

4 IN. (TYPICAL)

GROOVE TO RETAIN GLASS

TOP AND BOTTOM

NOTCH FOR DRAIN

BLACK CLOTH

FOIL LINING

CAULK ALL LOWER JOINTS

BAD WATER DRAIN

FRESH WATER DRAIN

HINGE

SCREWS AS REQUIRED

CRIMP TUBE AND INSERT THRU CAN BOTTOM

GLASS

REFLECTOR

SOLAR STILL

1 by 4 redwood sidepieces to the proper length, as shown in the drawing.

Drill two holes at each corner of the sidepieces and assemble with wood screws. The 1/2 inch plywood back may now be put in place and holes drilled for screws. Notice that no screws are put in at the corners, to prevent interference with those holding the sides together.

Mark the locations for the large holes that will receive the 1/2 inch tubing. Drill a 1/8 inch hole as a guide, and then drill three 5/8 inch holes and one 3/4 inch hole, as shown on page 77. Be sure the large hole is the proper size for the cap, which we'll solder to the end of the top tube.

The two drain holes can now be drilled, both of them 1/4 inch in diameter. One of these is located in the center of the bottom 1 by 4; the other is in the side 1 by 4, positioned at the vee formed by the bottom and plywood back. Study the drawing to be sure of locating this hole properly. The side drain can now be inserted.

This is a good time to calk the joints at the bottom and sides and apply several coats of sealer to the inside of the collector box. This is done to make it watertight, and so that the distilled water will run out the drain tube and not seep through the bottom of the box. Allow to dry thoroughly and check for leaks.

We know that any surface receiving heat will reradiate part of that heat. To prevent as much heat loss as possible, and also to present a smooth surface for condensation of water vapor, we line the inside of the box with aluminum foil. Running the foil in one piece across the plywood back and the bottom 1 by 4 will make an additional waterproof layer to help proper drainage. Notice that the foil extends into the bottom glass slot also.

Foil that is 24 inches wide will do the job in one piece. If it is necessary to use narrower foil, apply the section toward the drain tube first and lap the other section over it. Use glue, rubber cement, or airplane dope to apply the foil. Start at the top, carefully unrolling the foil for a smooth job. Let the edge of the foil extend a quarter inch past the edge of the glass slot. This excess will be forced into the slot later, when the glass is slid into place. Next line the inside surface of the other three 1 by 4's to complete the job.

Since some salty or otherwise undesirable water may not be evaporated before it reaches the bottom of the black towel wick, a vee-shaped trough is provided to catch this waste and prevent it from mixing with the distilled water at the bottom of the still. Made from galvanized iron, this 24 inch trough is a 90 degree angle with legs 1-1/2 inches wide. This can best be bent at the sheet-metal shop.

Drill a hole in the center of the angle, as shown, to receive the center 1/4 inch copper drain tube. Put the short length of tubing in place and solder securely. To keep the waste water from spilling out the ends of the trough, it is curved slightly by "crimping" the edges in several places.

Once the drain trough is completed, it may be installed by inserting the copper tube in the hole drilled for it. This should be a snug fit. Carefully punch through the aluminum foil first with a pencil, then press the trough down until it just touches the foil at the center.

We are now ready to start on the "wick" for the still. The 1/2 inch tubing used at the top and bottom to support the toweling is cut to size with a tubing cutter or fine hacksaw. Or ask your hardware dealer to do this for you, being sure to give him accurate dimensions.

In addition to holding the toweling in place, the top tube distributes water to the toweling. With a #50 drill, we drill two rows of holes at right angles to each other and spaced approximately 2 inches apart. These holes *do not* go through both walls of the tubing. See drawing for details.

The still uses a quart can as a reservoir. Cut the top from a large juice can and remove the paper. Next, cut a 4 inch length of 1/2 inch copper tubing and flatten one end in a vise or with a hammer. This tube will serve to meter the water into the long tube so that too much isn't fed to the toweling.

With a chisel, carefully cut a slit in the center of the can bottom. Force the metal inward until the flattened

Metal rods hold the towel "wick" in the foil-lined box of the solar still.

tube fits snugly with about 1/2 inch of it extending inside the can. Solder the tube in place, making sure it remains lined up.

Now slide the cap onto the far end of the drilled top tube and solder it in place. Push the tube through the holes in the box, being careful of the aluminum-foil lining. Prop up the box so that it is tilted back about 45 degrees from the vertical, and rotate the tube so that the two rows of #50 holes are properly positioned to feed water into the toweling when it is looped around the tube. The tilt of the still will vary with the position of the sun, so we are striking a happy medium in locating these holes.

With the tube in the right position, force the end cap into the 3/4 inch hole. This should be a snug fit and hold the tube in the proper place. Now solder the 1/2 inch elbow to the open end of the tube so that it points straight up. The free end of the tube soldered to the can is inserted in the elbow and soldered in place. Some water in the bottom of the can will prevent the joint at the can from melting while you work on the elbow.

Now attach a hinged 1 by 4 prop to the back of the box, using small wood screws as required. This supports the still and also adjusts the tilt to best face the sun. At this time also nail on the two legs, making sure to leave the proper one about 1/4 inch long so that water will run *toward* the fresh-water drain.

Smooth the ends of the bottom tube that will support the toweling and insert it in place. Now we are ready to sew the toweling together. The still uses a towel 24 inches wide, with the ends lapped and sewed in two places to make a loop. In measuring for this, make the loop slightly smaller than the distance between the tubes, because the towel will stretch somewhat when wet. Too much sag would cause it to touch the back of the box and thus contaminate the distilled water.

With the towel sewed together and dampened, slip the 1/2 inch tubes halfway out and start the towel loop onto the tubes inside the box. The bottom tube is slid back into place first; then the top tube is carefully raised into position and forced back into the 3/4 inch hole. Adjust the towel so that it covers the entire length of the tubes and is smooth. Do not let it touch the sides of the box.

At this point, remove the top 1 by 4 piece so that the dimensions for the glass can be taken. Slide a piece of cardboard into the grooves and trim to fit. Have your glass supplier cut the glass to measure. The grade of window glass known as "water-white" allows more of the sun's rays to pass than ordinary glass does and is therefore more efficient for our purpose. However, if it is not available, standard single-strength glass will do.

Slide the glass into position. Make sure it is clean, particularly on the inner surface, which will not be easy to reach when the still is assembled. Detergents may interfere with proper forming of droplets on the glass, so use plain water for cleaning.

Handle the glass very carefully to avoid cutting yourself on the sharp edges. With the still at a 45-degree angle, start the glass into the slots and ease it downward. When it contacts the aluminum foil at the bottom groove, it should force the foil neatly into place. Replace the top piece, tighten the screws, and the still is ready for operation.

Distillation is easy with the solar still. First, orient the still so that the sun's rays strike it as close to a right angle as possible. Mount the still on a level surface so

Operation of the solar still. Salt water poured in at top condenses on glass, as shown, and drains out at bottom.

that the uneven legs will give it the proper slant for draining. If the reservoir can is not vertical, carefully twist it until it is. The towel should be snug enough to hold it, and the force fit of the end cap in the 3/4 inch hole helps in this respect.

Now fill the reservoir, and to make sure that the still really works, add some salt to the water! After a few minutes the towel will begin to receive water from the distribution tube. If it doesn't or if the flow is too slow, very carefully open up the flattened tube in the bottom of the can with the point of an ice pick. Be cautious about this, however, as the water should not flow into the towel faster than it can be evaporated.

Heat from the sun is trapped in the box, and the black towel absorbs this. Water is therefore evaporated from the towel much faster than it would be normally. The vapor, free of all solids, recondenses on the smooth surface of the glass and the foil on the back and sides. You'll see this a few minutes after you put in the water; first the glass steams up, then droplets form and run down to the bottom.

Don't expect fresh water to gush from the still like a Niagara, but put a can or bottle under the drain to catch the distilled water. On a sunny day the still will begin producing soon after you set it in operation and will drip water steadily into the container. To guard against evaporation of this distilled water, some experimenters run a tube from the drain to a corked bottle.

At first you will probably reposition the still every

half hour or so for greatest efficiency. When the novelty wears off and you want to leave the still for steady operation, decide on a compromise tilt—your latitude plus 10 degrees or so—and aim the collector south (unless you live below the equator, of course).

To boost the capacity of your still use the reflector method described before. Make up one or more reflectors as with the water heater and attach them to the body of the still.

Addition of reflector panel increases yield of the solar still.

These three men are installing earth-water stills at Mount Mihara on Oshima Island.

THE SURVIVAL STILL

There is another kind of solar still, which is even more remarkable than those previously described. Called a "survival still" or "earth-water collector," this type draws moisture out of the ground, evaporates it, condenses it on a glass or plastic cover, and collects the fresh water in a container.

During World War II the Japanese needed a method

of producing fresh water on islands of the Pacific where none was available much of the time. Experiments were made with earth-water stills but no practical use was made of them. In the 1960's, however, a Japanese scientist named Kobayashi improved on the wartime experiments and designed a small portable still that produced a quart of water a day from the soil outside the Nippon Electric plant, where he was employed. Further tests showed that even in hot, dry deserts, the still produced some water.

In 1965, Dr. Ray Jackson and Dr. Cornelius van

Design of the survival still. Cactus or other water-yielding vegetation may be added under the plastic to produce more water. The plastic drinking tube permits water collection without dismantling the still.

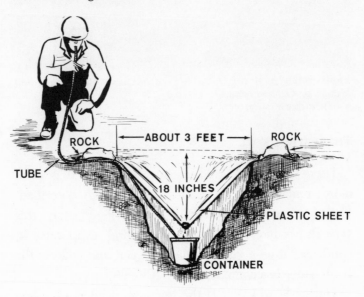

Bavel of the U.S. Department of Agriculture Water Conservation Laboratories in Tempe, Arizona, developed a much simpler survival still independently of the Japanese research. The Japanese had simply scraped off a bit of the top soil and placed their still on the ground. The Tempe scientists dug a conical hole in the ground and covered it with a sheet of plastic. Dirt from the hole weighted the edges of the plastic, and a rock or other weight formed it into a cone reaching down into the depression. The results were spectacular, and some test stills produced a quart of water or more per day for as long as a month at the same hole!

Refinements to the survival still include addition of a plastic tube to allow someone to drink the water without disturbing the still itself. It is also helpful to add cactus, other vegetation, or any material containing water, to the hole. For example, contaminated water can be poured into the hole and purified by the still for safe drinking.

You can easily make a survival still of your own, as shown in the drawing. Needed are a sheet of plastic of just about any type (although Tedlar is a "wettable" plastic and produces condensation in a film instead of droplets for faster production of distilled water), a length of small-diameter tubing, and a container of some sort. For storage, all the parts of the still can be kept in the container. Keep a survival still in the back of your car or in your plane, so if you ever need it you'll have it.

*Drinking from a survival still. These devices produce as much
as a quart of water a day.*

7

Radio

OUR PROJECTS so far have used the heat of the sun directly, and all have been quite easy to understand. In this chapter we take up a sun-charged power supply that makes use of the *photovoltaic* process, discovered by Antoine Becquerel in 1839. The conversion of light directly into electricity—with no intervening steps—is as fascinating as it is difficult to understand.

It was a long time from the discovery of the principle of photovoltaic conversion to its practical application. At first it seemed no more than a scientific curiosity because of its low efficiency. Early photocells used the element *selenium,* which derives its name from the Greek word for moon. This is an odd name for a material now used in so-called *sun* batteries. The selenium cell was first used in photographers' exposure meters, electric-eye devices, and the like. Present-day solar cells of selenium are inexpensive; their only drawback is a relatively low efficiency of conversion—less than 1 percent.

Pioneer experimenters with transistors used the element silicon, then switched to germanium. The unusual properties of silicon were remembered later, however, when efforts were made to develop a more efficient photovoltaic converter. Bell Telephone Laboratories produced solar cells with an efficiency of more than 6 percent. Bell then proved the usefulness of solar cells by powering rural telephone lines with sunlight. Then space applications took over and the solar battery became famous.

In a solar battery bundles of energy, called photons, penetrate the selenium or silicon and cause the movement of electrons through the material. If a wire is connected between the positive and negative terminals of the battery, current flows. This flow of current is similar to that in a dry cell, with one important difference. Nothing is added or taken away from the solar cell; it will produce current indefinitely instead of wearing out, as the dry cell will.

What this means may best be understood in terms of our space program. Conventional batteries are bound to wear out. But, barring damage from cosmic rays or some unforeseen occurrence, solar batteries will just keep operating—perhaps forever! In addition to their use in satellites, solar cells are used for radio transmission in remote locations and as warning beacons. Clocks and radio receivers operate twenty-four hours a

Artist's concept of a remote weather-reporting station powered by a large solar panel.
HOFFMAN ELECTRONICS CORP.

day, using solar cells coupled to storage batteries. The self-charging flashlight is another successful use of solar cells.

Solar-cell panels of many square feet are available commercially for tasks that justify the high initial cost. Solar cells are not cheap, even though silicon is one of the most plentiful elements. To be suitable for solar cells, the silicon must be ultrapure, and the raw material to make a sun battery is costly. The cell-manufacturing process is expensive too. It is helpful to remember, however, that the first cost of a solar battery is total cost.

The recent introduction of transistors and improved solar converters has made possible radio reception, and even transmission, with no power other than sunlight. In 1955, a message was sent from a sun-powered transmitter and picked up on a sun-powered receiver operated by radio hams. Our armed services and NASA have developed walkie-talkies, helmet radios, and emergency equipment powered by solar energy.

More recently, sun-powered transmitters have been sent aloft in satellites. Sun batteries also power remote radio installations and harbor warning beacons by charging storage batteries for round-the-clock operation. The advantages are obvious. No power lines are necessary, and solar batteries last indefinitely.

Now let's build a radio powered entirely by sunlight, or artificial light for indoor and nighttime use. Our radio makes use of a selenium cell that can be pur-

A possible use for the solar-powered radio. This experimental transmitter-receiver was powered by solar batteries mounted on soldier's helmet.

chased for as little as a dollar and a half or a silicon cell that costs slightly more. The practical application of solar-powered radio has passed far beyond the simple receiver described here; however, the easy-to-make little radio nicely demonstrates the use of the solar battery in electronics. The interested reader will find a large amount of material on more advanced projects in handbooks and in mechanical and electronics magazines.

MATERIALS:

B2M solar battery (or substitute)—one
audio transistor—one
IN34 diode—one
365 tuning condenser—one
Antenna coil—broadcast, one
Headphone—2,000 ohms or more, one
Plastic box—one
Phone jacks—two
Binding posts—two
Knob for condenser—one
Knob for antenna coil—one
Terminal board—one
Rubber feet—four
No. 24 hook-up wire, antenna wire, and 6-32 screws, nuts, and washers as needed

Most of the parts for the radio may be purchased at your local radio wholesale house or from a mail-order firm. You will be able to buy from the wholesaler if you tell him you are an experimenter and describe the project. The plastic case—a sandwich box or similar container—can be bought at the dime store. Prices will vary somewhat, but will be between five and eight dollars for all the parts, including the earphone. In case the exact parts specified in the list of materials are not available, the clerk will be able to provide equivalent items.

No attempt has been made to miniaturize the assembly of the radio, and the beginner will find it easy to put together. The various parts are spaced for easy connection of wires and ample room for the soldering iron. If desired, the radio may be built into a box onequarter the size of that shown on page 98. This chapter includes such a project but it is for those with some previous experience with radio work. Whichever plan of attack you decide upon, have all the parts on hand before you start work. You'll find that you can complete the radio in an evening, and start enjoying it immediately—using a lamp to substitute for the sun.

The first task is to drill all the mounting holes in the plastic box which will house the radio. Check the diameters of the phone jacks, binding posts, antenna coil, and condenser at the points where they go through the plastic, and drill holes of the proper size. For the larger holes it is a good idea to drill a pilot hole first and then enlarge it to the correct size. Be careful not to crack the plastic. If you do not have a large enough drill, use a round file to do the job.

Because the condenser shaft must protrude through the plastic cover, drill this hole first. Locate it according to the dimensions on the drawing, unless the condenser you are using is of much different size and shape. Place the condenser in the box and put the lid on it. Now turn the box over carefully, keeping the condenser properly located, and drill through the plastic and into the mounting holes in the condenser frame.

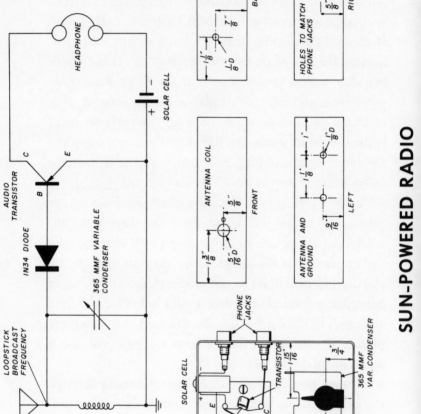

SUN-POWERED RADIO

This procedure ensures that all the holes will line up when it is time to assemble the radio.

Notice that the small hole drilled near the edge of the antenna-coil mounting hole must match the metal fitting on the coil. Use the metal mounting bracket included with the coil as a template to properly locate the small hole.

After all the holes are drilled, including those for the terminal board, clean up rough edges, remove chips from the box, and assemble the parts. Tighten the phone jacks and binding posts snugly, and use fiber washers with the 6-32 screws and nuts to protect the plastic. Snap the antenna coil into place and mount the solar battery with the glossy surface up.

With all the parts installed, do the wiring next. Follow the drawings carefully if you are not familiar with radio theory. The diode will probably be labeled with an arrow, like the one shown on the drawing, or coded in some other way to indicate direction. The center lead on the transistor is B, as shown in the drawing, and the lead closer to it is E. Make sure of the hookup of the diode and transistor and also that the sun battery's black wire goes to the phone jack.

Soldering the connections will give best results. However, since it is easy to damage transistors by over-heating, you may want merely to wrap the lead wires around the posts of the terminal board. While not as good an electrical connection, this method does work and was used on the radio in the photograph. If you do

The solar radio works indoors, too, using light from a window or lamp.

solder the transistor in place, pinch the transistor lead between the solder joint and the transistor with a pair of long-nosed pliers during the operation, to draw off surplus heat.

Now wipe up any excess soldering paste; check all joints and mounting screws for tightness. If everything is in order, put on the plastic top and mount the control knobs. If you were unable to find a knob small enough for the antenna-coil adjusting screw, use the cap from a toothpaste tube as shown in the photograph. Drill a hole slightly smaller than the screw and twist the cap onto the shaft. To make the adjusting screw easier to turn, carefully bend the spring clips away from the shaft. Paint the cap black to match the one on the tuning condenser, and the radio is complete.

This book is not the place for a technical discussion of the theory of radio, but we can briefly trace the radio waves that come through the air and are converted to sound in our receiver with the help of sunshine.

Radio signals are picked up by the outside antenna and carried into our radio. From all the signals in the air the desired station is selected by adjustment of the tuning condenser and the antenna coil. From this tuning circuit, the chosen signal goes through the diode "detector," which passes only that portion of the signal that we are interested in. This "audio" signal, still very faint, goes next to the transistor where it serves to trigger proportional, but much greater, amounts of power from the sun battery. This amplified audio signal activates the earphone and makes the music or the news broadcast we hear.

So much for theory; now to see how well our solar radio works. Attach an outside antenna to the proper binding post and a ground wire to the other post. The longer the antenna, the better, although the radio shown performed well with about 10 feet of wire and brought in several stations. It did a better job when connected to the TV antenna.

If you live many miles from the nearest radio station, you will have to use a long antenna. In extreme cases it may be necessary to increase the power of the radio by adding one or more solar batteries, connected to the original in series—that is, red wire soldered to black. This increases the voltage of the power supply.

In most cases the radio will bring in several stations nicely in bright sunlight. Use the tuning condenser to select your program and sharpen up the adjustment with the tuning coil. To fancy up the radio, add a broadcast dial, with appropriate frequency numbers drawn in as they are on a larger radio. You've probably noticed that there is no on–off switch, but don't worry about leaving this radio on all the time. There's nothing to wear out, and the power is free!

At night or on very cloudy days, you can tune in your favorite programs by placing the radio under a lamp. Don't place the solar battery so near the bulb that it becomes heated, as this may damage it. This should not be a major problem; satisfactory operation can be obtained at a safe distance from the lamp.

That's the solar radio. Good luck in building and using it; with care your set should give a lifetime of service. If the electronic side of solar energy appeals to you, there are many interesting projects you can work up: a code practice oscillator, for example, a continuous-wave (code) transmitter, or even a portable receiver that requires no external antenna.

SOLAR MITE

The solar radio is a challenge for the miniaturizer. So

a compact, "space-age" version of the basic design is given next. As you will see, the circuit is the same as the one used in the radio just described, but smaller components are used in some cases and the whole assembly is shoehorned into a tiny plastic box. Even though it is much smaller, the Solar Mite is a better performer since it packs its own collapsible antenna. The tuning dial is more attractive and has its own calibration.

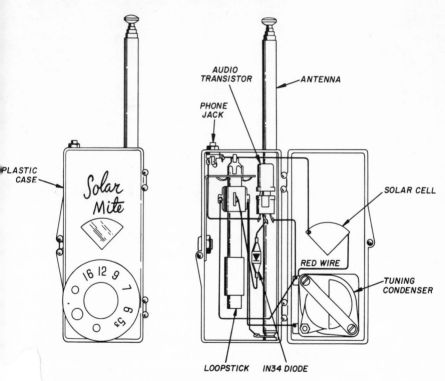

MINIATURIZED RADIO

Solar MITE *with antenna extended for outdoor reception.*

If your local radio supplier can't provide the necessary parts, check mail-order firms like Lafayette, Olson, Radio Shack, or others. The radio in the photograph is sprayed with orange Day-glo paint and is an eye-catcher. Don't paint the box cover, but cut a piece of orange paper to fit inside it. Letter as desired, and cut out for the solar cell. See page 103. The point of the cell acts as the station selector. The quarter-round silicon cell used in this project was broken from a round cell. Place cell on a magazine, tap lightly in center with a center punch and—presto! Four perfect quarter-sections, each big enough for a solar radio. Of course, a standard 1 by 2 centimeter cell may be used. Just cut a hole in orange paper to fit.

Indoors, the Solar Mite can be played beneath a lamp. A length of wire with alligator clips at each end can be used to attach the antenna to the lamp or to the phone for better reception.

CONVERT TO SOLAR POWER!

A one-solar-cell, one-transistor radio does not deliver the ultimate in performance, of course. But you can build more complex, higher-performance sun-powered radios. Check the electronics magazines for such projects. There is an even easier way to enjoy the fun and benefits of solar radio, however, and that is by converting a pocket transistor radio to solar power.

A single selenium or silicon solar cell will operate only a small earphone-type radio. Five silicon cells soldered together will provide ample power for the popular pocket-sized radios, and will drive the loudspeaker to plenty of listening volume. You can put together one of these solar "shingles" yourself, or buy it ready-made and covered with protective plastic. Some companies provide the solar pack with attaching wires and a mounting device.

If you plan to use a five-cell battery you will have about 2 volts to work with. This will operate a radio normally using two pencells, or 3-volt supply. For a radio using a 4.5 or 9 volt battery you will need more

ALL-SOLAR RADIO

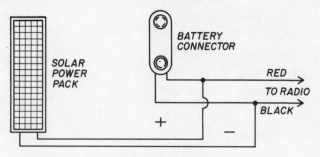

SOLAR OR DRY CELL

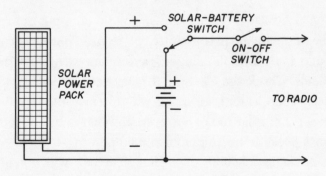

SOLAR-RECHARGEABLE BATTERY

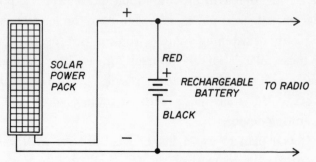

SOLAR CONVERSIONS

cells. Each solar cell delivers about 1/2 volt. The power packs offered by suppliers are available in 4.5, 6, and 9 volt sizes, so get one to match your radio.

In the simplest conversion to solar power, remove the conventional batteries and permanently attach the leads from the solar cell to the battery-box terminals. Now you will have a radio that will play when it is in sunshine or under artificial light of enough intensity. This is fine except during nighttime or cloudy weather, or when no light source is available indoors. You may want a more "sophisticated" solar radio.

By adding a two-way switch and leaving the dry cells in the radio you can have a set that uses the sun or artificial light when available but can be switched to conventional batteries when necessary. There is an even better method, and that is substituting recharge-able batteries inside the radio as the standby source of power. In this circuit, as the drawing shows, the solar battery charges the mercury batteries in the radio when it is not playing the radio directly. Here we have a very convenient and long-lasting power source. Instead of buying a new set of batteries every month or so, you tap the sun for power. Such a radio built by the author has operated on solar power and one set of mercury cells for several years. All that is necessary is to place the radio in the sun or under artificial light occasionally to keep the storage batteries charged and ready.

This transistor radio has been converted to operate on either conventional batteries or solar power, at the flip of a switch.

8

A Solar-Powered Airplane

FROM TIME TO TIME gullible people are swindled with engines that run on water instead of gasoline. An airplane that flies on sunshine sounds as farfetched, but the model shown in this chapter does just that. It is presented last, as the most advanced and intriguing project demonstrating the uses of solar energy.

Indirectly, glider pilots have been flying on solar energy for many decades. This is so because the sun heats the earth and produces helpful "thermal" currents of air that rise and carry soaring craft up with them. Our project is not a glider, however, but a powered craft. It mounts a tiny electric motor driven by an array of solar cells of a special kind. With the sun overhead, enough electricity is generated to drive the propeller fast enough to fly the plane. The fuel for this amazing model airplane is weightless—unless you can

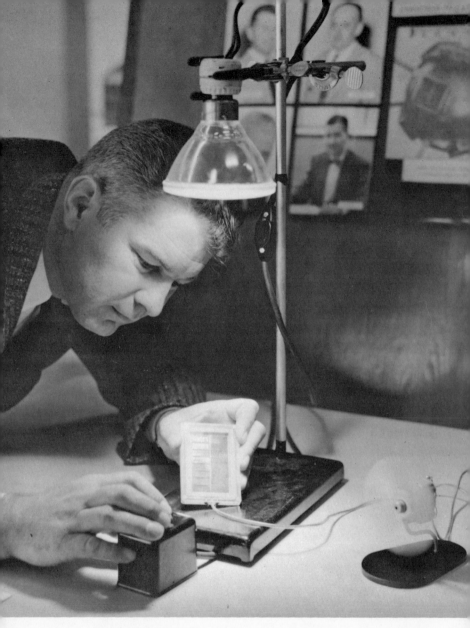

Germ of the solar-powered airplane. Engineer demonstrates conversion of light energy to power to drive a small electric motor and propeller.

U. S. ARMY PHOTOGRAPH

weigh a sunbeam—and the craft will fly as long as there is sufficient sunlight.

Soon after solar batteries were introduced they were used in a number of demonstrations. Some furnished power for electric motors driving the propellers of scale-model airplanes. While this made an eye-catching display, solar-battery manufacturers were quick to point out that their products were not being suggested to operate airliners! However, the idea of a solar-powered model airplane was inevitable.

The airplane presented here is one of a series of designs built during a period of several years. Overly optimistic about the amount of power in sunlight, I first built a conventional model plane with a wing area of some 200 square inches, and an over-all weight of close to 5 ounces. This sounds quite light, but it might as well have been 5 pounds, even with a total of 100 solar cells mounted atop the fuselage!

The successful version of the solar plane is simple in design and light in weight, to fly on sunbeams.

Sadder and smarter, I shrank the size of the craft, eliminated the heavy fuselage, and shaved weight in every other way I could think of. Each new design weighed less and crept nearer to the goal of sustained flight on sun power. But only when a new kind of solar cell (weighing about one-third as much as conventional silicon cells) became available was success achieved. Conventional solar cells are made from slices of high-purity silicon, "grown" in single crystal form in a molten furnace. There is also a solar cell made from cadmium sulfide, using the "thin-film" technique. A thin-film cell is deposited as a vapor on a suitable "substrate." Produced by Clevite Corporation, cadmium-sulfide solar cells are marketed in sizes up to 3 inches square, compared with the standard silicon cell only 1 by 2 centimeters. Furthermore, the cadmium-sulfide cell is only a few thousandths of an inch thick, flexible enough to be formed over curved surfaces, and only about one-third the weight of silicon cells of the same power output. Presently on the market are cells of 6 percent efficiency, only about half the maximum of silicon cells. However, the other advantages outweigh this shortcoming in many applications.

The 3-inch Clevite cells each produce about 300 milliwatts of electric power at a little less than 1/2 volt. Sliced into thirds and wired in series, two of them yield about 2 volts and drive a tiny electric motor and its geared-down propeller. To boost the craft's power, "solar-chargers" are added. These foil reflector panels—

similar to those we used on previous projects—concentrate more sunlight on the solar cells and up the power output considerably.

For the experienced model builder the solar plane will be easy to construct. Beginners will have to work a bit harder but the results far outweigh the work entailed in building the project.

MATERIALS:

3 inch cadmium sulfide solar cells (Clevite)—two
Micro-Mo motor 05L—one
four-inch propeller, plastic or wood—one

balsa wood:

1/8 by 1/4 by 18—two pieces
1/16 by 1/16 by 36—two pieces
1/16 by 1/8 by 36—two pieces
1/32 by 3 by 18—two pieces
Copper wire (single strand), 24 inches
Tissue paper—one sheet
Glue
Sheet metal for switch
Paper cement
Rubber bands
Timer fuse

The plane is built of balsa wood for light weight. The wood strips and sheets chosen should be a compromise

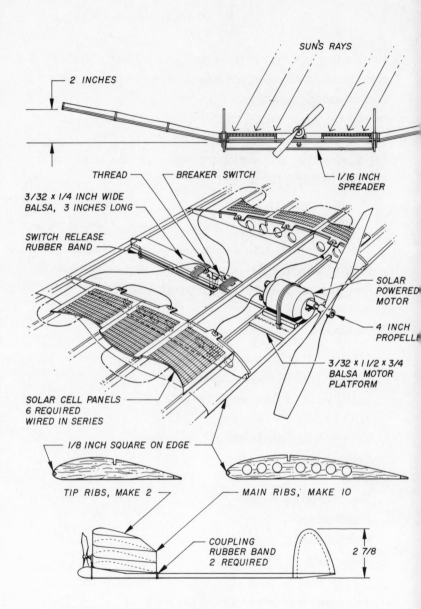

SUN'S RAYS

2 INCHES

THREAD

BREAKER SWITCH

1/16 INCH
SPREADER

3/32 x 1/4 INCH WIDE
BALSA, 3 INCHES LONG

SWITCH RELEASE
RUBBER BAND

SOLAR
POWERED
MOTOR

4 INCH
PROPELLER

3/32 x 1 1/2 x 3/4
BALSA MOTOR
PLATFORM

SOLAR CELL PANELS
6 REQUIRED
WIRED IN SERIES

1/8 INCH SQUARE ON EDGE

TIP RIBS, MAKE 2

MAIN RIBS, MAKE 10

COUPLING
RUBBER BAND
2 REQUIRED

2 7/8

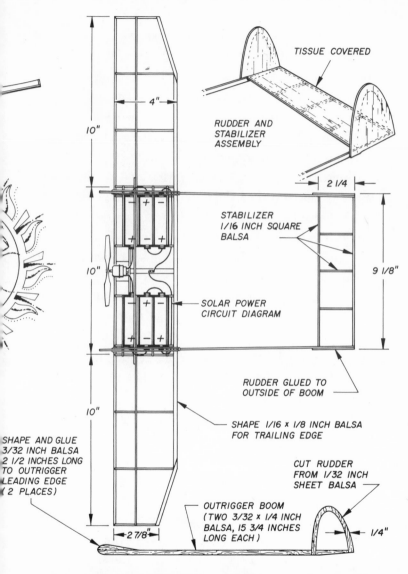

TISSUE COVERED

RUDDER AND
STABILIZER
ASSEMBLY

4"

10"

2 1/4

STABILIZER
1/16 INCH SQUARE
BALSA

9 1/8"

10"

SOLAR POWER
CIRCUIT DIAGRAM

10"

RUDDER GLUED TO
OUTSIDE OF BOOM

SHAPE 1/16 x 1/8 INCH BALSA
FOR TRAILING EDGE

SHAPE AND GLUE
3/32 INCH BALSA
2 1/2 INCHES LONG
TO OUTRIGGER
LEADING EDGE
(2 PLACES)

CUT RUDDER
FROM 1/32 INCH
SHEET BALSA

1/4"

2 7/8"

OUTRIGGER BOOM
(TWO 3/32 x 1/4 INCH
BALSA, 15 3/4 INCHES
LONG EACH)

SOLAR POWERED MODEL AIRPLANE

between weight and strength. The main wing spars should be hard and strong since they are stressed more heavily than the other members. The leading and trailing edges of the wings, the booms, and the tail surfaces should be of medium-hard stock. The wing ribs can be made of soft balsa. The ribs are further lightened with holes made by a paper punch.

Build the wing first. It is constructed in three separate panels and then the outer panels are glued to the center with the wingtips raised for the proper dihedral angle. While the glue on the wing joints is drying, make the stabilizer and the twin rudders, as well as the booms that attach the tail surfaces to the wing. Assemble the stabilizer to the booms and allow glue to dry. Carefully sandpaper the leading and trailing edges to a rounded shape; then cover the stabilizer with paper on the top side only. When this is done cement the rudders in place. Allow the glue to dry and then cover the rudders with paper on the outside only.

Add another coat of glue to the wing joints. Round off the leading edge and shape the trailing edge to a knife edge as shown. Sandpaper smoothly. The wing is now ready for mounting of the solar cells.

Trim off excess metal from solar-cell terminals, leaving only a small tab. The six cells are now glued to the ribs and strips. See pages 114–15. The polarity of the cells is reversed for easy wiring of the six in series. Attach the metal switch parts to the balsa mounting strip, as shown, wrapping thread and gluing for strength. A bent pin serves as a rear clip and this is glued to the trailing edge of the wing at the center section.

Make two small holes in the motor mount, just outside of the square retaining strips. The ends of a short rubber band slip through these holes and are retained by straight pins. The motor fits under the rubber band. To save weight, cut off all but a short length of the lead wires. We are now ready to wire up the solar cells, switch, and motor.

Unbraid some stranded copper wire and use a single strand to hook up the power plant. Use a small electric soldering iron and do the job carefully. The solar-cell terminals nearest the motor go directly to the motor-lead wires. Notice that one is positive and one negative. Do not solder the connection at the motor yet, as we want to be sure the motor turns in the proper direction.

Using a short length of hook-up wire join the individual solar cells. Notice that negative joins positive all down the line. When you have wired together three cells on one side, run a wire to one side of the switch. Then join the other side of the switch to the terminal of the rear cell on the remaining bank of cells. Be sure to continue joining negative to positive.

Now we can check for correct polarity at the motor connection. Attach a rubber band from the switch to the rear hook. With the wing in sunlight or under a bright lamp, touch the two leads to the motor terminals. If the propeller blows air toward the rear of the wing the polarity is correct. If it blows forward, rotate the motor 180 degrees and then solder the final connections.

The wing may now be covered with paper. Use tissue except for the space around the motor, which should be covered with a piece of typewriter paper carefully trimmed to fit. When the wing is covered, it may be sprayed with water to tighten the paper. As soon as the water dries the entire wing should be pinned down to a flat surface with the wingtips blocked up the proper amount to prevent warping. Don't forget about the switch protruding from the bottom of the center section—pin the wing down to a board notched for the switch.

For proper lift the wing must set at the proper "angle of attack." Glue a triangular piece of balsa wood to the boom at the point at which the wing attaches. When the glue is dry, assemble wing and tail, using rubber bands, as shown, to attach booms. Support the underside of the wing center section with your fingers to check the balance. The plane should be level, fore and aft, when supported at the main spar. This indicates that the center of gravity coincides with the center of lift. If the nose is low, move the wing forward and check again. If the tail is low, move the wing aft and recheck.

Test glide the solar plane in tall grass if possible so that it won't be damaged in case of a dive or stall. If the plane dives, move the wing farther forward. If it stalls, move the wing back. Increasing the angle of attack of the wing also has the effect of raising the nose in flight, and decreasing the angle lowers the nose. You may want to experiment by changing the triangular strip of wood under the wing.

When you are satisfied with the glide of the plane it is time for the crucial test flight—under power. However, there is a safety measure we must take first. A rubber-band-powered model airplane has a limited motor run. So does a gasoline-powered type; in fact any conventional fuel will last for a limited time. But we have powered our solar plane with a most *unconventional* fuel! Without some means of switching off the electric motor we would have no way of controlling our solar plane and it would fly until the sun went down. For this reason we need a flight timer of some sort.

The mechanical flight timers used on gasoline-powered model airplanes weigh as much as or more than our complete plane, so we need a lighter method. We'll use the much lighter fuse-type timer that contest modelers have used for years to bring their craft down after a certain duration in the air. With chemically treated fuse material available at model-airplane shops we have a simple and lightweight timer for our solar plane.

Start the motor by stretching a rubber band between the switch and rear clip. Cut a short length of fuse and insert it in the rubber band. Light it carefully—you don't want to set fire to the airplane! In fact it may be

The author and the finished solar plane.

wise to light the fuse before inserting it in the rubber band. When it burns to the rubber band it breaks the band and stops the motor. You can thus regulate the duration of the motor run by using fuses of varying lengths. A small square of aluminum foil glued to the underside of the wing will protect it from any danger of being ignited by the hot fuse. Another wise precaution is not to fly your plane over an area where the dropped fuse might start a fire.

When all systems are go, launch your plane gently into the wind. This is best done by holding the booms with both hands just aft of the wing. If you have done your job well and the sun is doing its part your solar plane is on its way. There may be further refinements of balance required and you may want to warp a rudder slightly to adjust the circling of the craft. Remember, the flatter the turn, the more power will be received by the solar cells.

Another way to increase the power is to mount "solar chargers," as shown on page 122. As with our other projects these should face out 30 degrees from perpendicular to the solar cells. Make the solar-chargers from aluminized Mylar on paper backing, or use 1/32nd inch sheet balsa with aluminum foil cemented to it. The center reflectors are joined together at the top. Outer reflectors are braced with thin strips of bamboo or balsa wood. Trim the edges that attach to the wing so that they fit the curve of the ribs.

Measured with a volt-ammeter, the solar chargers

Solar plane fitted with aluminum foil "solar-chargers."

added more than 25 percent to the power of the solar plane. Of course, as the sun drops lower the reflectors may do more harm than good by shadowing the solar cells. Maximum power will be available when the sun is directly overhead in summertime. "High noon" is a good description of solar-plane flying. The higher the sun, the higher your craft will fly. After the motor stops, there is still another kind of sun power acting on your plane when conditions are right. To guard against rising thermal currents carrying your plane away you may want to operate a "dethermalizer" together with the motor switch. This is done by hinging the front edge of the stabilizer of the craft so that the tail may raise and bring the plane down in a stall when the fuse burns through the rubber band.

Some years ago an engineer at Wright-Patterson Air Force Base patented a solar-powered airplane. With a wing made up entirely of solar batteries, this unmanned, instrumented research craft would fly at altitudes up to 60 miles above the earth! As yet, this full-scale solar plane has not been built, but who knows?

Recent developments in aviation include manpowered airplanes, in which the pilot not only works the controls but pedals powerfully to drive the propeller

Futuristic unmanned solar-powered plane for high-altitude research.
SOLAR ENERGY SOCIETY

too. It has been found that this "one-manpower" engine can lift a plane, so the dreamers of old weren't really on the wrong track after all. Let's extend this finding a bit. One manpower is only a fraction of one horsepower, and thus one horsepower should fly a lightweight plane nicely. How much solar energy does it take to produce one horsepower?

Each cell of your solar plane develops a maximum of about one-third of a watt. Three of them produce one watt; and 3,000 cells would produce one kilowatt. A kilowatt is about 1-1/3 horsepower, thus 3,000 solar cells would be ample power for a lightweight plane. And these 3,000 cells have a total area of less than 200 square feet, about that of the wing on present man-powered planes. Furthermore, they would weigh only a few pounds. The only major problem of a solar-powered *man-carrying* airplane would seem to be its cost—something like 45,000 dollars worth of solar cells. With such a price tag the project might well be called shooting for the sun.

In the meantime you can enjoy solar flight for only a few dollars. It might be good insurance to put your name and address on your craft and offer a reward for its return—just in case it gets away from you some sunny day!

9

More Solar Projects

THIS BOOK SHOULD be only a starting point for anyone interested in solar energy and its applications. The field is still new, with lots of room for enterprise and imagination. Why not take over from these last pages and develop solar projects of your own?

If we can fly a model airplane with sunshine, there are obviously many other projects we can power with solar energy. Among them are toy cars ("sunmobile" would be a good word), boats, window displays, and so on. You can track such things down in back issues of popular mechanics and electronics publications. Or you can dream up some of your own. How about a solar-powered dirigible, for instance, using a gas-filled balloon and a solar cell or two to drive a motor and propeller? It would be a good idea to tether the dirigible unless you want to set some long-distance records.

In the model-car field you might copy the Baker electric car that International Rectifier Corporation

Solar panel atop old electric car furnishes power to storage batteries. Silent, pollution-free operation impresses Central Park policeman.
INTERNATIONAL RECTIFIER CORP.

once operated with a huge solar panel mounted on the roof. Or you could build a simpler, gearless, prop-driven racer. Attached to a central pole or mounted on a track, such cars could be raced in competition.

The light from electric bulbs will power solar motors too—not as well as the bright sun, of course, but enough for some applications. A word of caution here would be not to place a hot bulb too close to solar cells, since high temperatures can damage them.

Just as we could operate solar radios on stored solar energy, we can run solar motors. The answer lies in the rechargeable battery. A circuit drawing is presented as an idea of what can be done to provide power around the clock if needed. Actual solar cells, secondary batteries, and motors used will depend on the particular

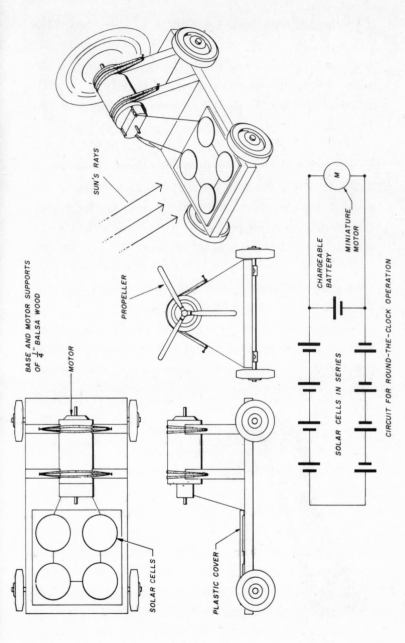

SUN'S RAYS

BASE AND MOTOR SUPPORTS
OF $\frac{1}{4}$" BALSA WOOD

MOTOR

PROPELLER

SOLAR CELLS

PLASTIC COVER

CHARGEABLE
BATTERY

M

MINIATURE
MOTOR

SOLAR CELLS IN SERIES

CIRCUIT FOR ROUND-THE-CLOCK OPERATION

SOLAR MOTOR

application you have in mind. The basic principle is the same: solar cells charge a chemical battery during the hours of sunshine to provide a reserve supply that can be used as needed.

There is probably a particular phase of solar work that appeals to you more than the others. If you are a radio or electronics fan, you'll spend more time on the chapter on the solar radios; then push on to a sun-powered transmitter or maybe a receiver with a loud-speaker instead of the simpler earphone used in the sets in this book. You can also build a variety of sun-operated relays or even a communication system that utilizes beams of light instead of radio waves.

If converting solar energy into mechanical power strikes your fancy, design and build a more powerful plant than the one presented here. Try a steam engine

Solar-powered flashlight uses sunshine to recharge batteries inside the case.
HOFFMAN ELECTRONICS CORP.

Four solar cells drive this model aircraft carrier in its swimming-pool ocean.
HOFFMAN ELECTRONICS CORP.

with a solar-fired boiler. Solar turbines and hot-air engines have been made, and some of these have been presented in popular publications in the mechanical field.

The science of optics is related to solar energy. Starting with the Fresnel lens used in our solar furnace, see what other projects you can devise. Try compound arrangements with other lenses and reflectors. Some experimenters might want to combine the Fresnel lens with the solar cell, thus focusing more light onto the cell for greater power output. The limiting factor here will be the temperature generated by the condensed solar rays. You might try a tracking mechanism to keep a solar furnace properly aimed at the sun throughout the day.

The amateur chemist might be interested in the solar still, or perhaps a sterilizing device using sun heat. One researcher realized that there was a loss of efficiency in his solar still when drops of water collected on the glass. His solution to this problem was a special nitric acid treatment of the glass. This permitted moisture to condense in a film instead, resulting in greater transmission of solar heat. Another solar-energy application is the culture of algae: a food supply that some people suggest as a partial answer to the problems of food shortages.

There may be more applications for the simple emergency survival still described in the book. This prin-

Use of a sun-powered shaver is one way to beat five-o'clock shadow.
SOLAR ENERGY SOCIETY

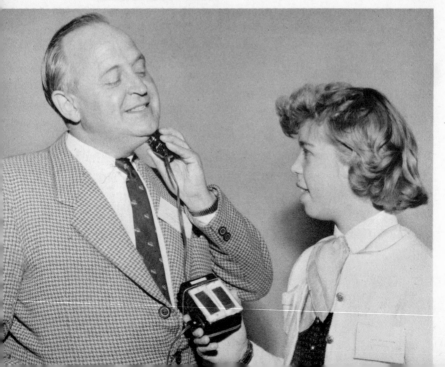

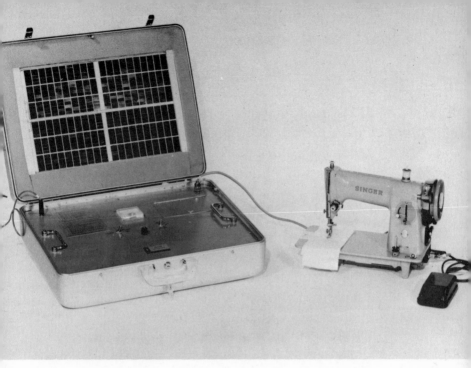

Since a stitch in time saves nine, why not take along this sun-powered portable sewing machine on that next trip?
SOLAR ENERGY SOCIETY

ciple has been suggested as a method of drying marshy ground and also for increasing the growth of plants.

For the experimenting gadgeteer, solar collectors can be made from discarded auto headlights whose parabolic shape is perfect for this purpose. A fire starter can be made from a flashlight reflector. The tip of a piece of kindling is held at the focal point and presto— a fire, courtesy of the sun. The same device will also light cigarettes and cigars, providing a safer light than matches in dry forest areas.

At the other end of the scale is a large parabolic reflector made from a surplus radar antenna or other appropriately shaped "dish." One of these would make a fine cooker or furnace, but keep in mind that the focal point may be very small and very hot. Once burned is twice careful, but that is a hard way to learn. Be careful too that you don't burn the bottom out of the cooking pot!

The solar device that probably goes back further in time than any other is the sundial. Although it is almost a curiosity now, it would be interesting and instructive to build one. Then be more modern and put together an electric clock powered by solar batteries.

Watch the newspapers and television for news of solar-heated homes or other such projects that may be built in your vicinity. If you are interested in architecture you already know how important the sun can be in helping to heat a home. Someday it will also be possible to cool buildings with sunshine.

Solar energy continues to have important applications in space. The sun is already providing the power for many of our lunar vehicles; perhaps it will soon operate power plants for the benefit of the first men on the moon. In the vacuum of the moon the sun's rays provide even more power than on earth, and the lunar day is two weeks long instead of only a few hours.

Perhaps the most poetic of all uses of sunlight would be that of "solar sailing" in space. In this book we present a model airplane driven by sunbeams and suggest, with tongue in cheek, a man-carrying craft powered by the sun. But some hardheaded space scientists have proposed to unfurl huge plastic sails and ride through

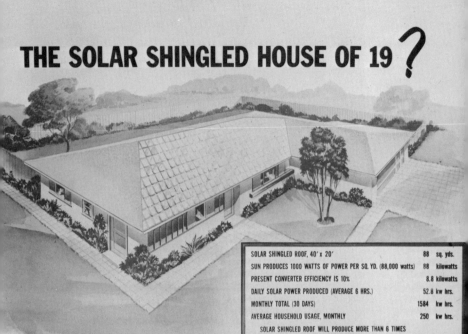

THE SOLAR SHINGLED HOUSE OF 19 ?

SOLAR SHINGLED ROOF, 40' x 20'	88	sq. yds.
SUN PRODUCES 1000 WATTS OF POWER PER SQ. YD. (88,000 watts)	88	kilowatts
PRESENT CONVERTER EFFICIENCY IS 10%	8.8	kilowatts
DAILY SOLAR POWER PRODUCED (AVERAGE 6 HRS.)	52.8	kw hrs.
MONTHLY TOTAL (30 DAYS)	1584	kw hrs.
AVERAGE HOUSEHOLD USAGE, MONTHLY	250	kw hrs.
SOLAR SHINGLED ROOF WILL PRODUCE MORE THAN 6 TIMES NORMAL REQUIREMENTS		

This fanciful solar home is not only heated, but is also provided with enough electricity for all household purposes. Solar "shingles" on the roof convert sunlight to energy.
HOFFMAN ELECTRONICS CORP.

Dr. T. C. Tsu studies a model of his solar sail.
WESTINGHOUSE

the endless reaches of space on the solar wind, a stream of tiny energetic particles. Whether such a dream will ever be reality is hard to say. But without it, there are still many wonders we will surely benefit from as science continues to make use of the bounty that is ours in the sun. Meantime, keep busy with the modest projects presented in this book.

The Sun
and Solar Energy

Mass of sun	332,488 times mass of earth
Apparent diameter of sun	864,000 miles
Temperature of sun surface, approx.	10,000 degrees F.
Temperature of sun corona, approx.	20 million degrees F.
Temperature of sun center, approx.	30 million degrees F.
Solar mass consumed, per second	4 million tons of hydrogen (to helium)
Total energy release by sun	0.38 trillion, trillion kw (3.8×10^{23} kw)
Energy reaching outer atmosphere of earth	170 trillion kw (170×10^{12} kw)

Proportion of sun radiation reaching outer atmosphere of earth	less than one thousand millionth
Energy reaching earth surface, approx.	85 trillion kw (85 x 10^{12} kw)
Solar energy received in United States, per year, approx.	9000 trillion kw-hr or 1150 billion tons coal

(Solar energy reaching Lake Mead is five times greater than the power generated by the hydroelectric generators of Boulder Dam.)

Firms Engaged in Solar-Energy Applications

Bell Telephone
  Laboratories
Murray Hill, New Jersey
  07971

do-it-yourself solar cell kit

Clevite Corporation
540 East 105th Street
Cleveland, Ohio 44108

cadmium-sulfide solar
  cells

Edmund Scientific
  Corporation
Barrington, New Jersey

Fresnel lenses
solar-furnace kits
survival-still kits
aluminum foil
solar batteries
electric motors

Education Materials &   solar-demonstration kit
    Equipment Co.
Box 63
Bronxville, New York

Elgin Watch Company   solar clock
Elgine, Illinois

Fabrite Metals Corporation   mirrors
205 E. 42nd Street
New York, N. Y. 10017

Hoffman Electronics   solar cells
    Corporation   solar-cell handbooks
El Monte, California

International Rectifier   solar cells
    Corporation   solar-cell handbooks
El Segundo, California

Dr. George Lof   reflector cooker
Farmers Union Building
Denver, Colorado

Solar Energy Applications   various solar products
    Laboratory
Melpar, Inc.
Falls Church, Virginia

Micro-Mo Electronics   small electric motors
Box 3952
Cleveland 20, Ohio

Howard W. Sams & Co., Ltd.
4300 West 62nd Street
Indianapolis 6, Indiana

Solar Cell and Photocell Experimenters Guide

Solar Products
Opa Locka, Florida

solar water heaters

Sundu Solar Heater
Mr. Anthony J. Meagher
3319 Keys Lane
Anaheim, California

solar heaters

Dr. Harry E. Thomason
6802 Walker Mill Road S.E.
Washington, D. C. 20027

solar homes
solar tepee

Yellott Solar Energy Laboratory
9051 North 7th Avenue
Phoenix, Arizona

solar instruments
research and testing

Zenith Sales Corporation
1900 North Austin Avenue
Chicago, Ill. 60639

solar radios

Bibliography

Daniels, Farrington, *Direct Use of the Sun's Energy*. New Haven: Yale University Press, 1964.

Halacy, D. S., Jr., *The Coming Age of Solar Energy*. New York: Harper & Row, 1963.

——*Fabulous Fireball*. New York: The Macmillan Co., 1957.

Solar Energy. Tempe: Solar Energy Society, Arizona State University.

Sun at Work. Tempe: Solar Energy Society, Arizona State University.

Index

621.47 Halacy, D. S.
H
    Experiments with
    solar energy

621.47 Halacy, D. S.
H
    Experiments with
    solar energy

DATE	BORROWER'S NAME
NOV 28	David Farch 14
MAR 7 1980	Jim Tubb 15
AN 30 1980	Jann Sk